Manifestations of Madness

Front cover: Emma Tice, aged 44, in 1877, a patient at the Norfolk County Asylum (Norfolk Record Office SAH267).

Manifestations of Madness

Women's Voices from the Norfolk County Lunatic Asylum

Julie Jakeway

POPPYLAND PUBLISHING

This edition 2021 published by Poppyland Publishing, Lowestoft, NR32 3BB.

www.poppyland.co.uk

ISBN 978 1 909796 85 0

Designed and typeset in 10.5 on 13.5 pt Gilgamesh Pro.

Printed by Severn.

Picture credits:

Bastenbas (CC BY-SA 4.0) 5
Costelloe, A 33
Flitcham Primary Academy 55
hoeandworthingarchive.org.uk 51
Ian, S (CC BY-SA 2.0) 61
McCrorie, B (CC BY-SA 2.0) 27
Norfolk County Council viii
Norfolk Record Office cover, 48, 50 (top), 58, 72
Park, C (CC BY-SA 2.0) 57
Private collection 41, 47
stavros1 (CC BY-SA 3.0) 61
Surrey History Centre 20
The Metropolitan Museum of Art (public domain) vi
Uczen, S 55
University of Dundee Archive Services 18
Walsingham Estate 36
Wellcome collection (CC BY-SA 4.0) 54, 69, 70, 76
wikiart (public domain) 64

Contents

Photo of an asylum patient c1850-1858 taken by Hugh Welch Diamond. Diamond was educated at Norwich School and later studied medicine at the Royal College of Surgeons. Specialising in psychiatry, he was appointed to Springfield asylum, the first Surrey County Asylum. From 1848 to 1858 he updated his predecessor's atlas of engraved portraits of the patients with photographs. He believed that mental states were manifested in the person's facial features or expression (physiognomy) and that photographs, as objective representations of reality, would show 'the passing storm or sunshine of the soul'.

Acknowledgements

I owe a huge debt of thanks to my son, Duncan Jakeway, who provided unstinting technical support for this project.

Thanks to Gill Blanchard, Sue Paul and other members of the Past Search community for their feedback and encouragement.

I am extremely grateful to those who gave permission for their images to be included, also to the consistently helpful archivists at Norfolk Record Office.

Julie Jakeway, 2021.

Note: Where the British pre-decimal currency system is found the comparative amount in decimal currency is shown in brackets using its 2017 equivalent based on the converter supplied by the National Archives—https://www. nationalarchives.gov.uk/currency-converter/# (accessed July 2020).

Drawn by J.B.Ladbroke.

COUNTY LUNATIC ASYLUM, THORPE,

NORFOLK.

Pub.d by P.Youngman Witham, Dec.r 10. 1825.

Eng.d by T.Barber

Norfolk County Lunatic Asylum.

Introduction

By the majority of the public, an asylum is regarded merely as a place of custody and security for those who are incapable of taking care of themselves, or who have been proved to be dangerous to themselves or others; this is not perhaps to be wondered at, since before the lunatic can be admitted into an asylum it has to be certified that he is dangerous, or unable to discriminate between right and wrong. Considered however, in its proper light, an asylum is an hospital for the treatment of mental disease but adapted to meet the varied and special requirements of individual patients.

THESE are the words of William Hills, medical superintendent, written in his Annual Report of 1864 which offers us a window into the viewpoint of the Norfolk Lunatic Asylum in the years of his administration.

This book records the experiences of women who were patients in Norfolk Lunatic Asylum during the years 1851 to 1870, including twenty-one case studies. The asylum opened in 1814, and was only the third purpose-built county asylum in England and Wales. Begun in 1811, the asylum was erected on five acres of land three miles from the centre of Norwich in the village of Thorpe St Andrew. It was situated on the main Norwich to Yarmouth turnpike road, providing good access and communications to the city centre.

The County Asylums Act 1808 allowed counties to levy a rate to build asylums, but the majority were slow to respond. Norfolk County Asylum opened in 1814, after Nottingham in 1811 and Bedford in 1812. Why was the county of Norfolk so quick to respond to the 1808 Act? Norwich is an ancient city and from the Middle Ages until the end of the eighteenth century was considered the second city in the United Kingdom after London. It was in fact the second city to provide special care for insane patients too; Bethlem hospital in London (erected 1674) being the first and the Bethel in Norwich (in 1713) the second, both charitable institutions. The Bethel was built by Mary Chapman, whose husband Samuel bequeathed money for her to build 'a hospital for the habitation of poor lunaticks'[1]. In the 1770s the Bethel was providing care for between forty and fifty mentally ill patients, and in 1771 the first general hospital, the Norfolk and Norwich Hospital, opened in the county. Both the Bethel and the Norfolk and Norwich Hospital were judged to be successful so when government legislation advocated a scheme specifically for the treatment of the mentally sick and needy,[2] the proposed Asylum provided an expansion of the medical provision already existing within the county.

Two other charitable institutions in Norwich, The Great Hospital and Doughty's Hospital, pre-dated both the Bethel and the Norfolk and Norwich Hospital. The Great Hospital was founded in 1249 for the benefit of aged priests, poor scholars, and sick and hungry paupers, and Doughty's Hospital, founded in 1687, provided shelter, food and water for the destitute.

In 1814, seventy patients, male and female, could be accommodated at Norfolk County Asylum but, when extensions were built in 1831 and 1840, that number doubled. Substantial later additions to the site meant that, by 1881, seven hundred patients could be cared for.[3] The county asylum was intended for pauper lunatics who had previously been detained in workhouses or had remained within their domestic situation. Private asylums and private lodgings had been available to some, but these were only used by those with families who could afford to pay for care.

From its opening, the name of the asylum changed several times from Norfolk Lunatic Asylum to Norfolk County Asylum in 1889; to Norfolk War Hospital in 1915; to Norfolk Mental Hospital in 1920 and finally to St Andrew's Hospital in 1923, reflecting the conventions of each historical era. The period covered in this book is the mid-nineteenth century so it will continue to be referred to by its original title, Norfolk Lunatic Asylum, as it was known then.

Asylums across England and Wales were designed for the insane and a certificate of insanity was required for each patient, who needed to be assessed as either suicidal or dangerous. In 1860, the charge for maintaining a patient within the asylum was 8s. 8d. (£496.69) per week in Norfolk. This was paid by the poor law authorities where each patient was resident and assessed to be as without the means to pay themselves.[4]

The largely rural county of Norfolk recorded significantly higher numbers of paupers than in England and Wales as a whole. Norfolk recorded 7 percent in 1861 whilst England and Wales together recorded 4.4 percent for the same year.[5]

By the mid-nineteenth century the economy of Norfolk depended chiefly on agriculture and the practice of 'high farming' had widely been adopted by those farming three hundred or more acres.[6] This involved chemical fertilisers being used to increase yields and drainage systems placed under the ground. As the system was adopted even more widely, it contributed to greater prosperity for farmers but was not reflected in farm workers' wages whose weekly rate 'was as low as 8 shillings (£32.07) in 1851, and did not reach 13 shillings (£40.70) until 1867'.[7] Budgeting to meet the needs of a family on such meagre wages was surely more than the most resourceful could accomplish and a figure of 2s. 0½d. a week is quoted as being the amount spent on food by an adult worker in

Norfolk, the lowest amount recorded in any agricultural county in the 1860s.[8]

In addition to poor wages, farm labourers also suffered poor housing conditions. In 1863 the *Norfolk News* provided a stark impression of the living conditions in the cottagers' homes. A typical cottage was described:

> two small, wretchedly ventilated and almost dark bedrooms, with slanting roofs coming down almost to the floor. This miserable hovel was occupied by J.R. and wife, five children and their grandfather, besides an illegitimate child of one of the daughters. ...In one of the upstair rooms sleep father and mother; while in the other, measuring only 11 ft. 6 in. by 7 ft. 7 in. sleep son 11, daughter 13, daughter 17, son 20, and daughter 23, as well as the child of the eldest daughter who was confined in this room less than two months ago in the midst of her brothers and sisters.[9]

Access to medical treatment increased during the early nineteenth century as the presence of general practitioners became widespread across the county in towns and villages, although treatment incurred a fee. Medical clubs were set up by guardians and medical officers in the 1830s. These were intended for all members of the labouring class whose income was less than 18 shillings per week and contributions were from 1d. per week for a single adult to 2½d. for a large family. 'In return, the poor got free medical treatment during illness, free vaccination against smallpox, and attendance for confinements at half the usual medical fees.'[10] These medical clubs were not a success because the fees were too high for the lowly paid to afford and later on Friendly Societies provided health insurance at a cost more within their means. Outdoor pauper patients in Norfolk were frequently given 'beef, mutton, wine and porter' by medical officers, suggesting that the paucity of their diet was a contributory factor in their ill health.[11]

So-called 'moral' treatment for mentally ill patients was adopted at the asylum in Norfolk, as in other counties, following its success at the York Retreat founded at the end of the eighteenth century by William Tuke and the Society of Friends (Quakers). Neither chains nor corporal punishment were tolerated at the Retreat and the comfort of the patients was of paramount importance.[12] It relied on providing asylum: a retreat from daily living where adequate diet, hygiene, rest and medical attention to physical ailments might aid recovery. In Norfolk, work therapy was an important factor in the regime and patients were encouraged to participate in tasks within the asylum, men on the farm and in the workshops, and women in the laundry or the wards, as well as sewing and mending, which were common tasks for women in their domestic routine.

Given the harsh conditions in which the poor carved out their lives, it is not difficult to envisage the despair they must have felt in the face of such grinding poverty. A brief respite in the County Lunatic Asylum from the unrelenting struggle to obtain food and shelter may have improved the physical and mental health of the destitute whose predicament had temporarily overwhelmed them.

Today mental health problems remain as prolific as ever: depression, stress, anxiety, an inability to cope with the requirements of modern living. The result of stress continuing to have the same effect although the causes may have altered in the last hundred and fifty years. Physical exhaustion and starvation are less likely to be diagnosed as causes of mental illness nowadays, yet the pressure of daily living continues to affect our society: intense media pressure has been identified as just one contemporary cause of anxiety and distress.

My focus in these pages is the women whose lives, through poverty, debility, and the stresses of everyday life, brought them to the asylum for a period of refuge, and how their lives evolved in the years that followed. In accordance with National Archives' guidance, I have used terminology found in the records themselves. These terms reflect the attitudes and language of the historical period in which these records were created and some would now be considered derogatory or offensive.

Notes

1   Frederick Bateman/Walter Rye, *The History of the Bethel Hospital at Norwich built by Mrs Mary Chapman in the Year 1713* (Norwich, 1906)

2   Cherry, S., *Mental Health Care in Modern England, the Norfolk Lunatic Asylum/St. Andrew's Hospital c.1810-1998* (Suffolk, 2003), p. 26

3   Ibid, p. 3

4   Norfolk Record Office SAH 130 (Master's Journal/Report Book March 1860-June 1861)

5   Digby, A., *Pauper Palaces* (London, 1978), p. 84. Figures for Norfolk based on population figures in 'Census Enumeration' and poor rate returns in Annual Reports of Poor Law Board. Figures for England and Wales taken from Webb, S & B, *English Poor Law History Pt. 2*, p. 1041-2

6   Wade Martins, S., *Changing Agriculture in Georgian and Victorian Norfolk* (Cromer, 2002), p. 75

7   Springall, L.M., *Labouring Life in Norfolk Villages 1834-1914* (London, 1936), p. 37

8   Ibid 5, p. 23

9   Ibid 7, p. 53

10   Ibid 5, p. 175

11   Ibid 5, p. 176

12   https://wellcomelibrary.org/item/b24952862#? (accessed July 2020)

Admissions

POVERTY haunted the majority of patients within Norfolk Lunatic Asylum, and Caroline Ebbage was a case in point:

> for the past half year she has been in a low state and this condition has much increased since her last accouchement, she has not had sufficient good food; a week since she took a great aversion to her infant, she wants a rope to hang the other children, she talked very incoherently and said she was to take the flesh off her bones, she refuses her food, has had but little sleep for this past week, and this morning attempted to pull the hair off her head. Want of proper nourishment is the supposed cause of this attack.

Caroline's story will continue on page 27 but this extract from her case notes gives a brief picture of the effect poverty had on generations of folk in the nineteenth century.

It should not be surprising that poverty was key to many of the issues affecting asylum patients when the institution was intended for pauper patients, yet in only nine admissions during the years 1851 to 1870 is poverty actually cited as the cause; work issues are named in the case of twelve patients, family troubles in twenty-nine, grief in eight, intemperance in thirty-nine patients and puerperal insanity, or postnatal depression, in thirty-five patients, bringing the figure to one hundred and thirty-two patients all experiencing mental health problems

Sans asile (Homeless) painted in 1883 by Fernand Pelez. Pelez portrayed social issues in a realistic style and here provides an insight in the life of an impoverished nineteenth century family.

that would now be attributed in some part to socially influenced causes. Factors involving work, family, intemperance and puerperal insanity are frequently linked, within the asylum, to the condition of poverty. When Rachael Cutting (see p. 66) was admitted in 1868 she had been earning four shillings and sixpence a week (£14.09) to maintain herself and her daughter, and on three occasions had attempted suicide. The combination of poverty, physical exhaustion and starvation was evident in many of the asylum's destitute patients. Even by the standards of the mid-Victorian era, poverty was a significant problem in the county of Norfolk.[1]

The 1845 County Asylums Act made it obligatory for local authorities to provide public asylums for all pauper lunatics. The Lunacy Commission monitored provision of asylum accommodation nationally on behalf of the Secretary of State. Asylum authorities were created locally to manage each county asylum. Known as Committees of Visitors, these were composed of Justices of the Peace representative of the boroughs within the county, and were the managing body of every county asylum, to whom the superintendent referred in matters of policy.

Between 1851 and 1861 Mr. Ebenezer Owen was superintendent of Norfolk asylum with Mr. Owen's son-in-law, Lewis Casson, acting as medical officer from 1854. During their term of office a therapeutic regime of hygiene, work and exercise evolved. In 1861 Mr. Owen retired and, after a brief interlude when Mr. Casson held the post of medical superintendent, Mr. William C Hills, MD, was appointed, and remained medical superintendent at the asylum for the next twenty-six years. Throughout these pages personal observations from William Hills' reports are included, giving some insight into the largely liberal and compassionate attitude that prevailed within the institution during the years 1861 to 1870 which come within the scope of this book.

One of the measures introduced by the 1845 County Asylum Act was the 'certificate of insanity'. It was provided by medical practitioners or poor law relieving officers and required for each admission to a county asylum. In the case of admissions from a domestic situation, medical practitioners filled in the documentation on the basis of their own evidence, with additional information provided by families or friends. The other method of admission was via the union workhouse where the certificate of insanity was completed by the poor law medical officer.[2]

After certification, a patient was removed to the asylum with a reception order completed by a local clergyman or magistrate, which listed personal information including name, age, marital status, religion, together with information relating to their history, such as the patient's age at their first attack; the number of previous attacks and whether the insane person was suicidal, epileptic or dangerous.[3]

Prospective patients needed to be assessed as suicidal or dangerous to meet the criteria for treatment in the asylum, and threatened violence was frequently noted in patients' symptoms on their admission to the asylum. Suicidal tendencies were often reported by relatives and asylum attendants were instructed to carefully monitor potential suicides, but very few patients attempted self-harm once within the asylum. Before her reception as a patient, Rachael Cutting had attempted three times to take her own life by hanging, by drowning and by strangling, but once in the asylum she made no attempt to self-harm and, after just one month in the asylum her mental state having improved, she was working steadily in the laundry.

Epileptic patients formed a sizeable group in the asylum and were amongst the number considered to be both dangerous and incurable. Their violent behaviour was usually limited to the duration of their fits when they were at risk of causing serious harm to themselves. This vulnerability was recognised and eventually night wards were created specifically for both male and female epileptic and suicidal patients, 'under the constant supervision of an attendant, whose whole time and energies shall be devoted to them, in each department.'[4]

Phthisis, more commonly known as tuberculosis (TB) or consumption, was responsible for one in four deaths in England and Wales at the beginning of the nineteenth century and was regularly seen amongst the patients of the asylum. Their poverty and malnutrition made them particularly susceptible and Caroline Ebbage (see p. 27ff) eventually succumbed to this misfortune. Tuberculosis is an infectious disease which usually affects the lungs where it is known as pulmonary TB. The symptoms include loss of appetite and weight, a persistent and progressively productive cough with night sweats and the coughing up of blood. The infection is spread by bacteria in the droplets from coughs or sneezes.[5]

Included in the admissions register was a column for the cause of insanity. The descriptions are frequently couched in non-medical terms—'want of work', 'poverty', 'dissipation', 'disappointment in love'—classifications reflecting perceived economic and social conditions of the time. A diverse mixture of causes are recorded. These conceal underlying and often undetected physical illnesses, as well as the spectre of poverty which haunted the majority. 'Domestic affliction', 'family trouble', 'drink and starvation' are phrases which have a homespun quality, placing them firmly in a domestic setting rather than a medical, investigative or diagnostic context and were applied to patients when identifying the cause of their insanity. Many of the 'moral' causes listed would

Shewing the Admissions, Re-Admissions, Discharges, and Deaths, from 1851, to the present date,
September 30th, 1870.

	Male	Female	Total
Persons admitted during the period of 19 years	856	1049	1905
Re-Admissions	194	233	427
Total of Cases Admitted	1050	1282	2332

Discharged or removed.

	Male.	Female	Total
Recovered	402	528	930
Relieved	50	71	121
Not Improved	43	40	83
Died	365	378	743

	Male	Female	Total
Total Discharged and Died during the 19 years	860	1017	1877
Remaining, Sept. 30th, 1870	190	265	455
Average numbers resident during the 19 years	154	187	341

Showing the Admissions, Re-Admissions, Discharges, and Deaths, from 1851, to the present date,
September 30th, 1870.

today be labelled as social or emotional—grief, old age, want of work and poverty. A high proportion of female patients were identified as having a gender-specific cause of insanity at a time when diagnosis was heavily dependent on physical appearance, conduct and symptoms reported by the friend or relative present at the time of the patient's admission. The case studies featured in the the third chapter focus on female patients whose mental disorder was attributed to these gender-specific conditions (see Appendix) and track the outcome of these patients both during and after their treatment in the asylum.

Many patients were admitted with an unknown cause during the period 1851 to 1870, emphasising that mental illness was still an enigma in the period, though a perusal of their case notes sometimes reveals a likely cause. Such was the case of Hannah Goodrum who was admitted with acute mania from an unknown cause being restless, noisy, singing and constantly undressing herself. She was described as violent and required constant watching, and could only be restrained by manual force. Included in her notes is the fact that she was far advanced in pregnancy and, six weeks later, she gave birth to a baby boy. Pregnancy and imminent confinement were not initially perceived as contributing to her mental condition. A month later in July 1868, Hannah's infant was removed from the asylum by her husband. It was the normal procedure for babies to be discharged to the care of the family if the mother required further recovery time

Showing the probable Causes, Apparent or Assigned of the Disorders in the Admissions, Discharges, and Deaths of the year.

CAUSES.	The Admissions			The Discharges.						The Deaths.		
				Recovered.			Removed, Relieved, or otherwise.					
	Male.	Female.	Total.	Male.	Female.	Total.	Male.	Female.	Total.	Male.	Female.	Total.
MORAL.												
Mental Anxiety	1	2	3	2	1	3	...	...	...	2	...	2
Religion	2	4	6	1	1	2	...	...	...	3	...	3
Disappointment in Love	...	4	4	...	...	...	...	...	...	...	...	...
Domestic Troubles	4	7	11	2	4	6	...	2	2	1	3	4
Excitement	...	...	...	1	...	1	...	...	...	...	...	...
Failure in Business	1	...	1	1	...	1	...	...	...	...	...	...
Fright	...	1	1	...	1	1	...	...	...	...	...	...
Death of Husband or Wife	...	2	2	1	2	3	...	...	...	...	...	...
Death of Mother	1	1	2	...	...	...	...	...	...	...	...	...
Rape	...	1	1	...	2	2	...	...	...	...	..	...
PHYSICAL.												
Disease of Brain	3	7	10	...	...	...	...	...	...	...	5	5
Dissipation	2	2	4	1	2	3	...	...	...	...	4	4
Puerperal	...	11	11	...	7	7	...	...	...	...	1	1
Intemperance	9	4	13	10	...	10	...	...	...	1	...	1
Hereditary	6	4	10	1	4	5	...	...	...	1	1	2
Injury to Head	2	...	2	1	...	1	...	...	...	3	...	3
Epilepsy	4	4	8	1	1	2	1	...	1	2	5	7
General Paralysis	3	1	4	...	...	...	...	1	1	4	...	4
Debility	5	7	12	6	2	8	...	1	1	1	2	3
Idiocy	4	...	4	...	...	...	...	...	...	...	1	1
Amenorrhœa	...	3	3	...	2	2	...	...	...	...	...	...
Senile Decay	1	5	6	...	...	...	...	...	...	1	4	5
Poverty	...	7	7	...	2	2	...	1	1	...	...	...
Imbecility	...	5	5	...	..	...	...	1	1	...	...	...
Marriage	...	1	1	1	...	1	...	...	...	...	...	...
Climacteric Period	...	...	...	...	2	2	...	...	...	...	...	...
Not ascertained	7	20	27	3	6	9	...	2	2	5	5	10
TOTALS	55	103	158	32	39	71	1	8	9	24	31	55

Showing the probable Causes, Apparent or Assigned of the Disorders in the Admissions, Discharges, and Deaths of the year; from Report of the medical superintendent with the accounts of the treasurer of the Norfolk Lunatic Asylum, for the year, 1869.

in the asylum.

Mary Ann Stowers (see p. 66ff), also with the cause of her mental breakdown unknown, came from Catton Asylum, a private institution. She had spent ten weeks there, after which, she was removed by her husband, 'not being the least improved and if anything worse'. Mary Ann's husband, James, was a merchant with the means to pay for her care making her one of the very few private patients to be treated in the county asylum. Her speech on admission was incoherent and she was constantly talking and gesticulating night and day. It was reported that (she) 'endeavours to escape from the house, tears her clothes, wets her things and bed, struggles with anyone who attempts to interfere with her'. On admission it was noted, by the medical officer, that Mary Ann's 'unsteady gait, hesitation and peculiar drawling speech, together with the tremulousness of the muscles of expression etc leads me to believe this to be a case of general paralysis'. It is essential to bear in mind that the emerging field of psychiatric medicine was in its infancy and this diagnosis came from the physical symptoms presented by the patient. The terms general paralysis and dementia were frequently used in the nineteenth century to describe a diverse range of maladies rather than the syphilitic infection which is now associated with such terminology.[6]

The medical classification of mental disorders in the mid-Victorian period fell into the following categories: mania, melancholia, dementia and idiocy, with mania further subdivided into acute mania, chronic mania, epileptic mania, puerperal mania, hysterical mania and suicidal mania. The appropriate classification was determined after diagnosis by medical personnel within the asylum, whereas the cause of insanity was presumed from information received at the time of admission. By applying medical terminology of the period to classify these mental conditions, patients were effectively removed from the domestic domain in which the more colourfully descriptive 'causes of insanity' placed them. For example, on admission Rachael Cutting's mental disorder was described as melancholia, but the cause was noted as 'over anxiety'.

Previous attacks of insanity were frequently noted in the records, though William Hills, the medical superintendent, made this comment in 1868:

Unfortunately whenever a person who has once been in an Asylum happens to manifest the slightest eccentricity, this feature of his disorder is made the most of, by the Master of the Workhouse and others who, I am sorry to say, as a rule, show for such cases more impatience than sympathy.[7]

It may be deduced from this that he felt such diagnoses hasty and an expedient explanation for their behaviour.

Casebooks were also an administrative requirement. These recorded the condition and progress of individual patients with a varying degree of personal and medical detail. The words of the patients were rarely written down and the records presented the version of events understood by asylum staff and formed by testimony provided by the patient's family, friends or neighbours, or from their own first-hand observations.

A reluctance to undertake housewifely duties was frequently taken as a symptom of mental disturbance in female patients. It was often quoted in their mental decline they had become lax in the care of their home and family:

Mary Skelton (see p. 29ff) 'had omitted to do what she had always done for herself and family and was obliged to have someone to help her in her ordinary domestic duties'[8] and Hannah Harvey (see p. 71ff) was the subject of attacks of great depression and an 'inability to attend to her household duties'. Working industriously in the laundry or the wards of the asylum was seen as a positive step towards recovery and was regularly noted in patients' records.

The question of inherited madness was seen to be of particular relevance and family history was always checked on admission. The notes of Elizabeth Coates (see p. 32ff) confirm: 'the predisposing cause is hereditary taint. Her mother died insane', whilst Elizabeth Drake's notes (see p. 40ff) point out 'Her mother and another relative were insane'. It was commonly accepted by doctors specialising in mental illness, or alienists as they were then known, that insanity was hereditary and therefore patients' case notes frequently include references to it, together with their physical appearance, and any history of epilepsy.

William Hills fulfilled his obligation as medical superintendent to record patients whose elderly kin had been inmates in an asylum, but set down his personal feelings in his annual report of 1863:

> Regarding the aged who are sent hither in their dotage, there can be no doubt they are better off in an Asylum ... Is it right however, that the rising generation of these decrepit persons should be branded with the stigma of "hereditary taint" from parents whose only malady was age and its attendant feebleness of intellect.[9]

Both the presence or absence of bruising was frequently documented to indicate whether the patient had been subjected to physical ill treatment or injury before their reception at the asylum. Violence was a familiar theme in the reports by family and friends at the point of the patient's admission—either threats of murder or self-destruction. Bearing in mind that admission to the asylum was dependent on the likelihood of dangerous and violent actions being committed by prospective patients, it is possible the risk was exaggerated in some instances.

There were numerous occasions where patients had acquired bruising and injury by their own unrestrained behaviour as in the case of Hannah Harvey who was described as unmanageable when she was admitted, noting the necessity to fasten her arms on the previous day. It was recorded, 'she has several scratches and bruises on her arms and legs and a bruise on the back', for which medication was prescribed.

On her admittance in October 1868 Jane Frost (see p. 37ff) was noted to have jumped out of a second storey window in her night clothes and smashed several of her neighbour's windows. Numerous parts of her body were badly bruised as a result. She was described as a strong woman requiring the close attention of two nurses during her first weeks in the asylum to restrain her from 'violent' attempts to escape.

Both phrenology and physiognomy were popular in the Victorian period among the emerging medical professionals and the general public. Phrenology was the belief that measuring the bumps on the skull could predict mental traits, whilst physiognomy was the view that a person's character could be determined by their physical appearance. Alienists believed phrenology, by recognising the areas of the brain that represented each of the twenty-seven mental faculties, gave the scientific basis for adopting a therapeutic regime when treating those afflicted with mental disorders.

Both of these pseudosciences were rejected by the early twentieth century, but during this period, many asylum patients' admission statements included observations relating to the shape of their heads as well as their facial characteristics. Emma Tice (see p. 46ff) on admission was described 'of tall stature, very spare habit of body and lymphatic temperament. Head small and narrow and high at apex.'[10]; Charlotte Royle (see p. 56ff), whose head was 'long and narrow', also had 'a spare habit of body', but a 'sanguine temperament'[11]; Elizabeth Coates (see p. 32ff) was 'of spare habit of body and nervous temperament. Dull uneasy countenance. Head not well formed'.[12] These frequent references suggest that physical features were thought to be of significance, although never actually alluded to again in patients' case notes after admission.

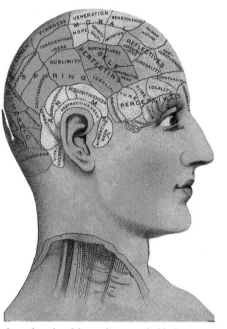

Phrenology head from The Household Physician, 1905.

Where misdiagnoses occurred, the symptoms exhibited were usually consistent with the cause attributed to the disorder and, given the unsophisticated means of interpreting illness at that period, it seems excusable that such mistakes might arise. It is essential to remember with reference to diagnosis and medication that 'asylum care cannot be evaluated on the basis of current day standards.'[13]

Life in an asylum in mid-Victorian England was a very different world to the one we inhabit in the twenty-first century. It was early days in the treatment of mental health and the language used to describe patients' symptoms and behaviour, that was acceptable then, would be abhorrent to us today. When reading the case histories the mores of nineteenth century society need to be understood. Terms such as 'idiot', 'imbecile', 'lunatic', are not ones in common use today, but in Victorian times they were used to describe a type of mental condition without the dehumanising connotations these labels evoke today. An 'idiot' was seen as having a congenital or inborn condition with a very profound intellectual disability and an IQ up to 30; the term 'imbecile' indicated a severe intellectual disability, perhaps as a result of injury or illness, with an IQ between 30 and 50.[14] Today, such disabilities would be described as physical or intellectual impairment. A lunatic, also termed *non compos mentis*, was 'sometimes of good and sound memory and understanding and sometimes not',[15] and therefore, in the nineteenth century, considered a suitable candidate for treatment and potential cure.

Notes

1   Digby A., *Pauper Palaces* (London, 1978), p. 84

2   Wright D., 'Delusions of gender?: lay identification and clinical diagnosis of insanity in Victorian England', in J. Andrews and A. Digby (eds), *Sex and Seclusion, Class and Custody: Perspectives on Gender and Class in the History of British and Irish Psychiatry* (Amsterdam, 2004), p. 158

3   Ibid, p. 159

4   Norfolk Record Office SAH 28 (Annual Reports 1844-1876)

5   https://www.sciencedirect.com/science/article/pii/s095461110600401x (accessed June 2020)

6   J. Melling and B. Forsythe, *Politics of Madness, The State, Insanity and Society in England, 1845-1914* (Abingdon, 2006), p. 131

7   Norfolk Record Office SAH 131 (Medical Superintendent's Journals July 1861-March 1878)

8   Norfolk Record Office SAH 264 (Female Case Book December 1865-April 1870)

9   Ibid 7

10 Norfolk Record Office SAH 262 (Female Case Book March 1853-August 1861)

11 Ibid

12 Ibid

13 Cherry S., *Mental Health Care*, p. 52

14 https://en.wikipedia.org/wiki/Idiot (accessed July 2020)

15 https://www.oireachtas.ie/en/visit-and-learn/history-and-buildings/historical-documents/approaches-to-mental-health/ (accessed July 2020)

Life within the Asylum Walls

IN 1842, when Norfolk Lunatic Asylum was inspected by the Metropolitan Commissioners in Lunacy criticisms included 'the amount of mechanical restraint used on patients, insufficient heating, the poor dietary, and the shortage of tables and utensils for meals.'[1] Changes were needed and by 1846, in addition to coal fires, new heating pipes had been installed to improve the comfort of staff and patients, ensuring that the temperature rarely dropped below fifty degrees Fahrenheit. Additional bathrooms were installed so that patients were bathed individually and daily, rather than twice weekly. At the next inspection it was noted that 'all the leg-locks and chains had been removed from the seats and benches in the day rooms and airing courts', and in 1853 all forms of mechanical restraint had been removed. In Norfolk the asylum had left behind the inhumane methods of the eighteenth century when physical containment and restraint were in regular use and had moved towards a more enlightened regime of therapeutic care and treatment.

The three best physicians: Dr Diet, Dr Merryman, and Dr Quit; three doctors representing diet, cheerfulness and rest, defend their patient from death.

The first Annual Report in 1854 by the medical officers of the asylum described the clothing provided for women patients:

> warm under garments with neat print dresses and linen caps; some are allowed to continue their own apparel where it is thought that a change will have a prejudicial effect.

For the men who had recently worn fustian:

> a neat grey cloth had been introduced; and in future we recommend that this material be generally adopted in the winter. Most of the patients are now supplied with flannel next their skin as we are anxious that the warmth of the surface be constantly maintained.

In the same report the medical officers pointed out that they frequently prescribed wine, brandy, ale and porter to patients as being the best 'tonics and restoratives'. By 1854 the food allocation had been defined clearly and for male patients breakfast was 1.5 pints of oatmeal milk broth, or porridge as it is now known, half being new milk, and 6oz of bread; for supper men were given 6oz of bread and 2oz of cheese with a half-pint of beer. Both men and women had the same midday meal; on three days this was 4oz of meat and 12oz of vegetables, mainly potatoes, with bread and a half-pint of beer, on the other days 10.5oz of meat pie or meat dumplings was served with 12oz of vegetables, the meat specified as 2.5oz without bone. In addition, 'for out-door workers, artizans [sic] and laundry women etc, ½ pt beer with bread and cheese at 11 am and 4 pm' was allocated.[2] Four shillings (£16.04) was allotted for each patient's food per week, twice the amount that Norfolk farm labourers were able to spend.[3]

The same medical officers in their first Annual Report were critical of 'some asylums' where the food allocation had been reduced for patients who were inactive, with the following observation:

> we entirely object to the idea that persons who vegetate in the wards should have only just food enough to keep them alive; if such treatment were adopted the health and comfort of those who are "feeble-minded", would be embittered, their lives shortened, and every prospect of recovery taken away.

When Elizabeth Baker entered the asylum in July 1859 with a diagnosis of puerperal insanity she was said to be 'anaemic looking'. The immediate cause of her illness was suggested as overwork and general debility.[4] For Elizabeth the daily rations at the asylum were more substantial than she was likely to have had at home: for breakfast the female patients were given 5oz of bread with butter and three-quarters of a pint of tea, and again for supper tea, bread and butter. Her midday meal of meat and vegetables with bread and beer probably constituted a more generous diet than she was used to. After the birth of her child, at the beginning of the month, she had been weak and frail, this regular nourishment was just what Elizabeth needed.

FOOD.

Butchers' Meat,	3777 st.	.	.	1312	18	7
Flour	1860 st.	.	.	151	7	6
Bread	2901 score.		.	545	7	4
Cheese	120 cwt. 1 qr. 21 lbs.		.	375	19	10
Tea	1000 lbs. .	.	.	172	16	8
Sugar	.	.	.	84	19	0
Coffee	.	.	.	23	5	3
Rice and Arrowroot	.	.	.	6	9	9
Groats	.	.	.	10	0	0
Salt	.	.	.	2	2	3
Milk	8028 gallons	.	.	267	13	4
Butter	3728 pints	.	.	254	8	6
Eggs	.	.	.	13	5	7
Sundry Articles of Grocery		.	.	37	12	0

	3258	5	7

Carried forward   £6203 10 3½

Food purchased during 1859 in Annual Report published 1860 from Report of the medical officers and superintendent, with the accounts of the treasurer of the Thorpe lunatic asylum for the year 1859 / [Norfolk Lunatic Asylum].

The day began for Elizabeth and all the asylum patients at half past six when they were provided with facilities for washing themselves, though the precise details of these washing arrangements were not explained. Those patients unable to manage for themselves were given practical assistance by staff. Breakfast was at eight o'clock and, on Sundays, Tuesdays and Fridays a devotional service was held half an hour later. At nine o'clock work began for those fit for employment and in fine weather everyone else capable of taking exercise was encouraged into the grounds for out-door activities. Patients engaged in physically strenuous employment had a break for refreshments at eleven o'clock.

At half past twelve all patients returned to the wards and dinner was served at one o'clock. At two o'clock employed patients returned to their work and at half past two unemployed patients went back to the grounds for exercise until five o'clock in summer and four in winter. Refreshments were distributed at four to those working and supper was served to all patients at six o'clock. After supper, reading, music, card-playing and other amusements were encouraged until bedtime which was eight o'clock in summer and seven in winter.

Although work therapy was perceived to be an important aspect of moral treatment, opportunities were restricted in the early years by the lack of suitable tasks available. After acquiring thirty acres of farmland in 1853, male patients worked in the gardens and on the farm, also as painters, carpenters, tailors, upholsterers and shoemakers. The number of items made and repaired by those working as shoemakers and tailors was impressive as can be seen from the list published in the Annual Report of 1859.

Work was seen as therapeutic because it provided a mental focus and prevented patients dwelling on their problems; it was a means of maintaining previous job skills and sometimes developing new ones. By 1860 over half of the one hundred and fifty-two men and three-quarters of the one hundred and eighty-eight women patients were working.[5] The output of the female patients

NORFOLK COUNTY ASYLUM.

ARTICLES MADE AND REPAIRED BY THE MALE ATTENDANTS AND
PATIENTS DURING THE YEAR 1859.

SHOEMAKERS.

LIST OF NEW WORK.	LIST OF REPAIRS.
33 pairs of Men's Leather Boots 4 pairs Men's Leather Shoes 16 pairs Women's Leather Shoes 61 pairs Women's Leather Boots 7 pairs Men's Duffle Boots 38 pairs Women's Duffle Shoes 5 pairs Women's Duffle Boots	276 Pairs of Boots and Shoes, soled, heeled and welted 90 pairs of Boots and Shoes, soled and welted 35 pairs of Boots and Shoes soled and heeled 81 pairs of Boots and Shoes soled 106 pairs of Boots and Shoes heeled 367 pairs of Boots and Shoes repaired

TAILORS.

LIST OF NEW WORK.	LIST OF REPAIRS.
11 Frocks 18 Pairs Braces 22 Mattresses, hair 1 Cushion Fibre 2 Curtains, blue serge 1 Knotted Rug	1013 Jackets 740 Waistcoats 1014 Trowsers 141 Frocks 3 Mattresses 32 Carpets bound 66 Mats bound 50 pairs Duffle Boots bound, and sundry repairs to padded room

Articles Made and Repaired by the Male Attendants and Patients during the year 1859; from Report of the medical officers and superintendent, with the accounts of the treasurer of the Thorpe lunatic asylum for the year 1859 / [Norfolk Lunatic Asylum]

engaged in needlework in the year of 1859 was equally impressive: 305 shirts; 45 tablecloths; 312 handkerchiefs; 360 sheets; 215 pillow cases; 160 shifts; 184 gowns; 308 caps; and many more garments too numerous to list. Just a month after her admission, Elizabeth was well enough to do a little needlework. Women also frequently worked in the laundry or as cleaners. Steam-powered washing machines, wringing machines and drying rooms had been established 'partly because the labour of the patients in connection with washing … is not regarded a desirable occupation for them.'[6] Elizabeth was not strong enough for laundry work; she had suffered an injury to her left knee some years previously and her leg swelled if she continually stood or walked. This understanding and acknowledgment of physical incapacity reflected the humane approach usually shown to patients by asylum staff.

In the mid-nineteenth century there was very little medication available for either mental or physical disorders and the most commonly prescribed remedies were revealed in the patients' notes: opium and morphia for pain relief; zinc ointment for the treatment of skin conditions; digitalis in cases of epilepsy and general paralysis, and the sedatives: chloral, bromide and laudanum.

Outings were organised regularly and an excursion by train to Lowestoft was arranged in the summer of 1859. Soon after Elizabeth Baker's admission in August that year, a total of 247 patients, 123 men and 124 women, left the asylum in Thorpe at eight o'clock to board the train at Norwich Thorpe station arriving in Lowestoft at around nine o'clock. A schedule which sounds quite an achievement even by today's standards. 'Railway staff and harbour authorities at Lowestoft afforded all the facilities in their power for the successful conduct of the undertaking'[7] and the day was proclaimed a success and enjoyed by all.

An annual pattern of events emerged during the 1860s: visits to the circus at Castle Hill in January; visits to Tombland Fair in March and April; cricket matches against Norwich grammar boys in May; picnics at Postwick Grove in

Patients on an outing with Asylum staff from Montrose Royal Asylum.

June; harvest treats in the cricket field in August; evening entertainments by minstrels in December; Christmas festivities in the hall with dancing and singing with a comment by William Hills, in 1866, that 260 patients had 'retired at 10 pm expressing their regret that Xmas does not occur 3 or 4 times a year'.

These activities and the recreation provided for patients after supper, in the form of music, cards or games may have been a luxury few had experienced in their day-to-day lives outside the asylum. Weekly and monthly periodicals were provided and it was declared that the two volumes of the *Illustrated London News* supplied to each ward proved 'a source of endless interest to patients'.[8] It is not known whether Elizabeth Baker had acquired the ability to read and enjoy the indulgence of monthly periodicals, but music and cards provided entertainment for those without literacy skills. In winter a fortnightly ball was held with a brass band providing the music where 'the patients pass merry evenings in dancing and singing'.[9]

In addition to these regular events there were also *ad hoc* entertainments from time to time: a magic entertainment for patients in May 1866; the Choristers cricket club played the asylum team in June 1866, afterwards giving an evening entertainment in the hall; there was cricket at Spixworth in August that year; General Tom Hewett's entertainment in September, and in February 1867 the

LUNATIC'S BALL.
Somerset County Asylum.

Mentally ill patients dancing at Somerset County Asylum.

patients assembled in the hall for an 'Optical Diorama'. In February the following year the patients were treated to an entertainment performed by amateurs and described by William Hills in his Superintendent's Report as follows:

> vocal and instrumental music, recitations, a reading from Pickwick, [and] closing with a "Comedy on Marriage". Patients evinced great delight by frequent and hearty plaudits.

In the summer months cricket matches, country walks, picnics and river trips were part of the asylum routine, giving patients opportunities for socialising in a manner they may never have enjoyed before.

When the Lunacy Commissioners inspected the asylum in 1861 they noted the paintings on the walls, the framed engravings, mirrors and ornaments which added to the cheerfulness of the wards, day rooms, bedrooms and dormitories. The greenhouses with aviaries, plants and flowers all contributed to the well-being of the patients.[10] Efforts to improve the ambience of their surroundings were continued by William Hills and his wife, who became matron of the asylum. Mrs. Hills regularly requested, and was granted, sums of £5 or £10 from the bazaar account to improve the 'ornamentation and comfort' of the buildings.

Brookwood Hospital Asylum Band.

The routine of the asylum day: the fixed hour of rising, orderly meals, regular work and exercise, and the unchanging hour of bedtime, were all considered essential contributory factors to the physical health and also the mental well-being of the patient.[11]

Susanna Sargeant, a single girl aged 24 and a governess by occupation, was admitted in February 1870.[12] On admission the cause of her insanity was unknown, but she was diagnosed with mania and the history of her behaviour as reported by her parents during the preceding six weeks was quite uncontrollable: 'she has now quite lost her reason and shouts, laughs, making grimaces, recites, gesticulates, and at times is quite incoherent, her movements are ceaseless'. By March she had 'become much quieter and more manageable', and on 30 March the case notes recorded that she had:

> decidedly improved, being more natural in conversation and behaviour, obedient and inclined to be industrious and tidily in habits. She is a source of some

annoyance to her fellow patients and the nurses, as she persists in correcting any mispronunciations or grammatical errors that they make.

By July on Sunday afternoons Susanna was playing the harmonium and leading the singing in the chapel, and was considered a great acquisition to the asylum community. In September, after seven months treatment, Susanna was a notable loss to the asylum when she was discharged on probation.

Whilst most patients hoped for an early discharge so that they might return home there were some who preferred the relative comfort of the asylum. Jane Frost (see p. 37ff) was admitted in October 1868 at the age of forty-nine with a diagnosis of acute mania, the cause attributed to the menopause. In July 1870 she was to be discharged, but it was recorded in her case notes:

> Owing to a bilious attack, which she much exaggerated, it was deferred until another month. She complains of frequent headache which she magnifies and is always able to enter into amusements and one of the first to request to participate in any treat! She evinces no desire to return home and is too fond of her present quarters.

Jane Frost was frightened she would be discharged without the means to support herself but once reassured that an allowance would be paid whilst she readjusted to life outside the asylum Jane became reconciled to her release.

In the early years of the nineteenth century patients in both public and private mental institutions were often subjected to physical restraint, severe overcrowding and were also likely to be exhibited to the general public for amusement and for the institution's profit. These practices had been eradicated by the middle of the century and the regime followed in Norfolk was humane and benign.

There were occasions when care standards failed to meet the expectations of the medical superintendent, William Hills and his assistant, the medical officer William Taynton. In May 1869 when the superintendent was on his morning rounds he witnessed an attendant 'using an idiot patient roughly'. William Hills recorded that the attendant had lost control and struck out at the patient's head several times, fortunately without having actually hit him. He said that other incidents 'had previously transpired (which I had been unable to prove) showing he was unfit for the post so I summarily discharged him'.[13]

Another episode occurred amongst the female staff which warranted William Hills' intervention. Several female patients complained to him of an attendant's harshness and 'great want of forbearance when they were excited'. She was also dismissed with a month's notice.

These incidents of sub-standard treatment triggered prompt action on the part of the medical superintendent confirming the asylum's commitment to maintaining high standards of patient care in an era which is not remembered for its compassion.

Notes

1   Cherry S., *Mental Health Care*, p. 55
2   Norfolk Record Office SAH 28, Annual Report 1854
3   Digby A., *Pauper Palaces*, p. 23
4   Norfolk Record Office SAH 262 (Female Case Book March 1853-August 1861)
5   Ibid 1, p. 66
6   Ibid 1, p. 67
7   Annual Report 1859
8   Annual Report 1866
9   Ibid.
10   Annual Report 1861
11   A. Campbell Clark, C. McIvor Campbell, A. R. Turnbull, and A. R. Urquhart, *Handbook for the Instruction of Attendants on the Insane* (London: Baillière, Tindall & Cox, 1885), pp. 48-50
12   Norfolk Record Office SAH 264 (Female Case Book December 1865-April 1870)
13   Superintendent's Journal Norfolk Record Office SAH 131

Case Studies

BIOLOGICAL factors were highlighted in the nineteenth century in an attempt to explain the incidence of insanity in women, and the debate concerning the female malady, as it was termed, continues to be of interest in the twenty-first century. Victorian psychiatrists held the view that 'women were more vulnerable to insanity than men because the instability of the reproductive systems interfered with their sexual, emotional and rational control'.[1]

Following childbirth women are vulnerable to moods that today are recognised as postnatal depression, but in the nineteenth century these unexpected moods, ranging from 'baby blues' to more serious postnatal depression, spoilt the maternal image which society had become programmed to expect. Coventry Patmore epitomised the mid-Victorian vision of domesticity in his poem *The Angel in the House*, which was a best-seller in its day, portraying the idealised wife whose mission in life was to provide comfort, affection, and unwavering support to the head of the household, her husband. This was the era of separate spheres for men and women; men's sphere being in the public, or working world, and women's in the domestic and family focused domain.

These values filtered down through the social classes and even at the lowest level, where poverty and depravation was the norm, society demanded that women continue to fulfil their domestic role even when overcome by exhaustion and malnutrition. Whilst women's issues at significant times in their lives were being recognised by the medical profession, treatment differed between the classes. Middle-class women were more likely to be treated in their own homes, and were frequently advised to avoid unnecessary strain, such as, reading or writing, or activities that were considered over-taxing to their brains.[2] Working-class women on the other hand, frequently undernourished and physically exhausted, were provided with more basic needs by the county asylums,

Puerperal Mania in Four Stages.

which was sometimes enough to enable them to recovery.

The recognition of women's vulnerability postpartum resulted in increased rate of admissions among women experiencing specific female events such as accouchement, lactation, parturition, puerperal fever and menopause. During the period 1851 to 1870, these conditions were often referred to in layman's language, causes of insanity being recorded as: confinement; childbirth; miscarriage; pregnancy; suckling child. All these terms are found in the patient records at the asylum. Individual case notes suggest their physical condition, already weakened by hard labour and malnourishment, was frail and the substantial demands of parturition and lactation further drained their strength. Mary Ann Neal was typical. She had previously been a patient when the cause of her breakdown was overwork, anxiety and poverty. Now, in February 1865, the mother of nine children and far advanced in her pregnancy, she was admitted suffering with delusions just days before the birth of her tenth baby.[3] One week later she had 'gone on very nicely since her confinement'. Three weeks later she was 'doing well and most industrious, sewing all day' being discharged in May 1865, recovered.

There were other gender-specific causes of insanity in addition to those directly linked with childbirth: amenorrhoea, change of life, climacteric, hysteria, menorrhagia, and uterine disturbance. Together, these accounted for a significant percentage of female patients at Norfolk Lunatic Asylum in the period under review. The speed with which some patients recovered their mental and physical health within the asylum is quite astonishing, bearing in mind there was rarely, if any, medication involved in their treatment. This success seems to confirm the sentiments of William Hills, as he recorded in the Annual Report of 1863:

> The earlier patients are placed under medical [care] the better; in cases of insanity, this rule is of vital importance, as the neglect of it, converts a curable condition into a chronic one requiring permanent residence. The average residence in the asylum of those, who recovered, is about 5 months, the longest was three years.

The provision of regular meals, comfortable accommodation, bathing facilities and clean clothing met the basic needs of those patients who were living in dire conditions, and this was sometimes enough to restore their mental, as well as their physical health.

The case studies that follow focus on patients with gender-specific conditions recorded at the asylum in the years between 1851 and 1870 (see Appendix). Some of the causes described were specific to certain years as shown in brackets. Their use abandoned as medical terminology developed, particularly following William Hills tenure, beginning in 1861, and may have been in measure due to his influence. One or more case studies is provided for most of the gender-specific conditions treated and includes additional details of the patients' lives both pre- and post-treatment in the asylum.

Accouchement (1867-1870)
The action of giving birth to a baby.

Accouchement was a term sometimes given to childbirth in the nineteenth century and was commonly used in Norfolk for three of the twenty years under review. This cause was attributed to Mary Jane Lemmon's case when she was admitted to the asylum in October 1869. Mary Jane was born in Acle, Norfolk, in January 1848, the daughter of Thomas and Sarah Lemmon.[4] Thomas was a coach painter, a skilled occupation in which he continued to be employed throughout his life. Their eldest son, John, was apprenticed to a drapery business in Lancashire by the age of seventeen, and Mary Jane was in London by the age of eighteen. Though her occupation at the time is unknown, it seems likely that her parents found her an opening with equally favourable prospects as her brother.

Sadly, circumstances changed for Mary Jane. Still single, she became pregnant and returned home to Acle for the birth of her baby in the summer of 1869, when she had a difficult labour and was physically ill afterwards. Despite her physical weakness, she immediately found another job in London as a domestic servant and returned there. After a very short time her new employer contacted Mary Jane's father with the news she was showing signs of mental disturbance: talking incoherently, refusing food and restless by day and night. He immediately went to London to bring her home, and on the train journey back to Norfolk she attempted to jump from the window.

The Street, Acle.

When Mary Jane Lemmon was admitted to the asylum on 4 October 1869 the cause of her illness was described as accouchement, an archaic description for giving birth. On admission it was recorded that there was no hereditary disposition and she was free from bruises. Mary Jane continued ill, both physically and mentally, initially suffering with chest pains, then reacting most vehemently when the assistant medical officer entered the ward: 'she started up from her seat, clung to one of the nurses and hiding her face burst into a series of convulsive sobs'. She explained later the reason for this reaction was due to the resemblance between the assistant medical officer and the man who had seduced her, thereby causing her great distress.

Mary Jane was encouraged to join in social activities as these were an integral part of patients' rehabilitation. In November she attended one of the fortnightly balls held at the asylum, with music provided by the asylum brass band, where dancing and singing gave the patients an opportunity to enjoy themselves in a communal activity. However, Mary Jane became hysterical with excitement the following day and was directed to bed. A similar episode occurred in June the following year. After a dance held at the asylum; she became very excited and attempted to escape.

Throughout the following year, Mary Jane had a variety of physical ailments: in January a severe cold and constipation; in May sickness and pain in the region of ovaries and uterus; in September episodes of fainting and constipation; in October headache, congested haemorrhoids and sickness; in November spitting blood and discomfort in the chest. However, by the end of March 1871, after seventeen months confinement, she had improved physically and mentally and was discharged as recovered.

Five days after leaving the asylum, on 2 April 1871, Mary Jane is recorded on the census return as living in the household of her aunt Elizabeth Thompson, aged 59 and single, in Sutton Road, Ingham, Norfolk. She was listed as Mary J, aged 22 and unmarried. In addition, at that address were Elizabeth's brother-in-law William Osborn, aged 70, and sister Anne Osborn, aged 61, as well as her niece, Mary Jane. None of the residents have an occupation listed, all recorded as being of 'Independent' means.

Ten years later at the time of the 1881 census on 3 April, Mary Jane had moved to Lancashire and appeared in the household of John Lemmon, her brother, living at 39 Doddington Street, Salford, with his wife Louise, who was born in Switzerland, and children: Lilly aged 13, a pupil teacher; Amy aged 11, Edith aged 9, Nellie aged 5, all scholars; and Elise aged 2. Mary Jane, then aged 32, is described as a domestic servant. There were two more residents: Marie Belguin, aged 42, a machinist who was John's sister-in-law; John Wright, aged

33, described as a boarder and farmer and Joseph Paton, a visitor aged 39, from Scotland whose occupation was ship's steward.

Kilmacolm Old Kirk, May 2016.

Was Joseph Paton the link between Mary Jane Lemmon and William Robertson Roy whom she married in Kilmacolm, Renfrewshire on 17 April 1881, only two weeks after this census?[5]

How Mary Jane and William met remains a mystery. Only a fortnight before they wed, Mary Jane was living in Salford with her brother, and William was living in Row, Dunbartonshire, with his brother-in-law, though both were quoted as resident in Kilmacolm at the date of their marriage.

Ten years on Mary Jane had moved back to Salford and was living at 18 Barnsley Street, with husband William Roy aged 46, a foreman joiner, and children, William aged 7, born in Scotland, Victor aged 3 and Wilhemena aged 1, both born in Salford—a positive outcome after an early period of misfortune. Mary Jane's death, from bronchitis, occurred in Salford, Lancashire in 1901, at the age of 51.

During the seventeen months Mary Jane spent in Norfolk Asylum she was ill in both mind and body, but eventually recovered her health. The child she had borne in 1869, just weeks prior to her admission to the asylum, was named Malcolm and remained in Acle in the care of Thomas and Sarah, Mary Jane's parents.

෨෦ଔ

When Caroline Ebbage entered the asylum for the first time in January 1868 the cause of her mental breakdown was also attributed to accouchement, the youngest of her five children being just two months old.[6] She did not sleep well at night, she would not speak, she often 'burst out crying' and asked for her sister and mother. Caroline's mother had lived with Caroline and her husband in the early 1860s but had died in 1863. The case notes state that she had no sister but, in fact, her sister Amelia had died early in 1867, a few months before Caroline's recent confinement, so it was not surprising that she would still be mourning her loss, particularly at such a susceptible and emotional time.

After four months Caroline was still 'unable to settle to employment of any kind'; she laughed 'idiotically and immoderately'. When her husband James, an agricultural labourer, visited her it was observed she abused him, also on two occasions during the night, she had 'some kind of stoppage'.

Nine months after her admission, Caroline was convalescent and wept when she thought how she had denounced her husband and children. Her spirits were 'buoyant', she had a 'merry' expression, which James said were natural to her. She was discharged as recovered at the end of November 1868.

Her re-admission occurred in January 1870, the cause being lactation when once again she had an infant to breastfeed. Her two-year-old daughter had died only a few weeks earlier in 1869, and her husband James reported they were short of food and parish relief had been stopped (a claim refuted by the local Justice of the Peace). After a matter of weeks in the asylum, with regular food and rest, she improved once more and within a month was working in the laundry where she was 'industrious' and in a natural state of mind. It was noted that one night she had a very severe epileptic fit. Was the 'stoppage' noted during her first admission also an epileptic fit?

After only three months she was declared fit and was discharged as recovered in March 1870.

Caroline's third admission to the asylum came in January 1871 when she was within a fortnight of confinement with her seventh child. Since her previous admission it was noted she had suffered several epileptic seizures; she had become incoherent, raving and violent and needed several people to restrain her. The cause of her breakdown, on this occasion, was said to be the worry of all her children having measles, whilst she was heavily pregnant herself. It was noted that on the day following her admission Caroline experienced labour pains and gave birth to a boy who was named Albert.

Caroline's condition showed no improvement after the birth of Albert, she had more epileptic fits and, in April, it was noted she had an habitual cough. Albert was sent home to South Walsham in April in accordance with normal practice when a patient had given birth in the asylum. Already Albert had remained in the asylum longer than most infants born there. At the end of the year Caroline was diagnosed with phthisis and moved to the infirmary. In May 1872 William Taynton the medical officer noted:

This poor woman is perceptibly breaking up, is now very emaciated and the cough gives her great anxiety, keeping her from sleeping or from lying down.

And in June:

Has been sitting upright all night as she says she cannot breathe in any other position. Yesterday she was in a semi conscious state for about an hour and was thought to be dying.

On 14 June 1872 it was noted she died from phthisis pulmonary, or TB as it would be described today. Phthisis or consumption, as it was also known, was virulent in the nineteenth century and was responsible for a quarter of all deaths at the beginning of the 1800s.

Married in 1858, Caroline had borne seven children in twelve years, in extreme poverty. The fact

La miseria (the misery) painted by Cristóbal Rojas (1886) depicts the social aspect of the tuberculosis, and its relation to poor living conditions. Rojas was to die from the disease in 1890.

that the family had been granted parish relief at one stage was an indication of their dire circumstances.

Amenorrhoea (all years)

The term used to describe a lack of 'periods' (menstrual cycles) in women.

In the years between 1851 and 1870, nine women were attributed with the cause of amenorrhoea (the absence of 'periods' or menstrual cycles). One was Mary Skelton, aged 29, the wife of a labourer living at Southery, Norfolk, and the mother of seven children, only three of whom were still living.[7]

Mary was admitted on 8 June 1869 and the background to her illness was provided by her husband. He said she had become ill a year earlier, shortly after the birth of her last child when she began needing help with ordinary domestic duties. The inability to cope with housekeeping was frequently quoted by family and friends as a symptom of the patient's affliction. Her husband reported she suffered with sleeplessness and would rise at intervals during the night to wash her hands; she refused to change her clothes or engage in any work, seemingly due to an exceptional fear of fire. Just a month earlier she had threatened suicide. On being told she was to be removed to the asylum she threatened to stab her sister.

It was understood there was no hereditary predisposition and she appeared to be in good physical health, also free from bruises that would indicate physical ill-treatment or injury before reception into the asylum. It was recorded that

Mary had not menstruated for 'a long time', which appeared to be the cause of her illness. Having been ill for a year, only two days after her admission she menstruated and afterwards showed no symptoms of insanity. It was reported she was most industrious working in the laundry and continued 'in the same satisfactory condition' until she was discharged at the end of July 1869.

Mary's life is well documented through the ten-yearly census records. In 1861 she was living with husband Richard, a farming labourer, at Little London in the parish of Southery. Mary and Richard had one son, John, aged 1 in 1861. Their household also included Richard's mother and brother—Ann Skelton a widow, aged 63, and George Skelton, a lodger, aged 22.

A year and a half after Mary's sojourn in the asylum, the family had moved to Essex and were living at Marsh Farm Cottage in Tillingham, where Richard was recorded as a decoyman. Their family comprised John aged 11, Mary aged 9 and George aged 2, all the children having been born in Southery where they had previously lived. Another daughter, Sarah Ann Elizabeth, born in 1870, had died within weeks of her birth.

In 1881 Richard was still employed as a decoyman in Tillingham, by which time John had left the family home. George, now aged 12, remained with his parents, working as an agricultural labourer, with additional younger siblings, Richard aged 9, Elizabeth aged 8, Clarissa aged 5, Robert aged 3, and another Skelton daughter just one week old, yet to be named. Mary and Richard named their last daughter, Mary Jane, after her sister who had died in 1878 at the age of 16. Sadly the second Mary Jane died as an infant, just one year old.

The parish of Titchmarsh in Northamptonshire was the family home in 1891. Richard continued as a decoyman, with son Richard aged 19, now a farm labourer, Elizabeth aged 18, now a domestic servant, Clarissa and Robert, aged 15 and 13 respectively, without an occupation recorded.

Twenty years later, in 1911, Richard and Mary had returned to Tillingham where Richard, whose skill was still valued, worked as a decoyman at the age of 77, their grandson living with them by then—Albert Richard aged 16, a farm labourer.

Richard Skelton was one of the Lincolnshire Skeltons, a family well known for their skill in creating decoys for catching ducks. His grandfather George had moved from Lincolnshire to Norfolk in 1807 where he formed a decoy on overgrown marshes belonging to a Mr Huntingdon of Somerton. George Skelton claimed he needed just two and a half acres of marsh to construct his decoy which locals thought ludicrous. However, George was undoubtedly successful and his reputation established when he took 1,100 teal in seven days.[8]

Trapping or decoying ducks was done by either luring them with feed or using a dog, sometimes a combination of both. Tame ducks, were set onto the pond and food would be scattered there attracting the wild fowl. After a time the decoyman would give a signal that the tame ducks had learnt to indicate more food

Entrance to a decoy pipe, with dog at work and wild fowl following him up the pipe, by Sir Ralph Payne-Gallwey.

would be found at the far end of the pipes into which they duly swam. The dog, known as the piper, on a signal would also go ahead up the pipe barking and appearing excited. Apparently wild ducks are very curious creatures and they would immediately follow the dog and tame ducks to see what all the fuss was about. The decoyman would watch and, if necessary, join in to encourage the ducks on to their fate. Richard was well taught, becoming accomplished at an art that served him well his entire life.

Mary gave birth to another six children after her short interlude in the asylum— some thirteen pregnancies in all. She recovered to live a long and fruitful life as the wife of this successful decoyman.

Change of Life (1855-61)

**Known as the menopause, when menstrual periods cease.
A term first used in 1761 and when applied to patients at
Norfolk Lunatic Asylum it implied emotional symptoms, such
as memory problems, irritability, or rapid changes in mood.**

This description of the menopause, in use since the eighteenth century, is still used colloquially today. It was a term used for six years in the Norfolk Lunatic Asylum records to describe women who were going through the menopause. Its use in the case books suggested emotional disturbance, such as memory problems, or rapid changes of mood. Rebecca Utting was admitted to the asylum in April 1855 at the age of 56 and is one of the first patients to be designated with this particular cause of insanity.[9]

It was her second spell in the asylum 'after a lapse of 8 or 9 years and is doubtless caused this time by change of life'. At the time of her admission it was confidently identified as the cause of her mental disturbance, possibly purely on the basis of her age. Rebecca was the wife of a carrier and her previous attack had been brought on by anxiety for her husband's business. Some years earlier

Former Wheatsheaf Inn, Corpusty.

her husband had been landlord of the *Wheatsheaf Inn* in Corpusty. Running a public house demanded the attention of both husband and wife, so Rebecca had always been closely involved in the day to day business that provided their livelihood.

She had been quite well and able to conduct her duties until a fortnight before when 'she began to wander about, talk extravagantly about her great wealth and threatened violence to her husband and once did throw the poker at him'.

After two months she was still described as being 'mischievous', which had a more malignant connotation than we now associate with the word, being frequently used of patients who were unruly and hostile. The usual asylum routine of regular meals, physical exercise and useful employment was provided for Rebecca and in a very short space of time resulted in her recovery.

By July she was described as industrious and in August as looking very well. Rebecca was discharged, recovered, at the end of September 1855 and at the time of the census, in 1861, was living at home in Corpusty with her husband James, and their unmarried son Edward, who was working with his father as a carrier and dealer.

∽◯◌

Two years after Rebecca, Elizabeth Coates was admitted, another patient with the cause attributed to change of life.[10] Elizabeth was forty-four, single and a servant living in Northwold where she had been in service until three months previously. On admission it was noted she had been active, steady and 'never shewed any symptoms of insanity before'.

She was diagnosed with suicidal melancholia which had been coming on for about four months and for which she had already received medical treatment. She conversed rationally on most subjects but 'talks about making away with herself, knows it is wrong, but the impulse seems not controllable by her reasoning faculties when it comes on'.

About six weeks after her admission, at the regular dance held at the asylum, Elizabeth 'escaped notice for a time and was not found until dead, being suspended by a small piece of tape to some railings' in the airing court.

Artificial respiration was applied but after a quarter of an hour it was accepted that all hope was gone. At the meeting of the coroner and jury, the verdict confirmed 'the said Elizabeth Coates came to her death by hanging herself and though they attached no blame to anyone they recommend the removal of the railing from the female airing court'.

A contemporaneous example of an airing court shelter at West Park, Epsom.

A tragic conclusion to Elizabeth's life and one of the few successful suicide attempts at the aslyum between 1851 and 1870.

Childbirth (1850-1852)

The process of giving birth to a baby.

Childbirth is only recorded as a 'cause of insanity' during the first two years (1851-1852) of the period of study. Terminology varied throughout those twenty years—accouchement; confinement; parturition were all used to describe childbirth in the records. Elizabeth Westgate, eighteen years old and single, was one such patient. Childbirth is described as the cause of her breakdown when she was admitted, in December 1851, six weeks after the birth of her baby.[11] She had received no treatment and was extremely feeble and emaciated, her speech profuse and incoherent. Her most prominent symptoms were a 'small to rapid' pulse, 'glistening' eyes, and 'an increase of temperature about the head with occasional hectic flushes'.

Medication was prescribed for Elizabeth and 'congestive symptoms of the head' indicated the need for occasional leeching, which involved the application of a living leech to the skin in order to initiate blood flow or deplete blood from a localized area of the body.[12]

This was a common treatment in the nineteenth century and frequently prescribed. There followed this note: 'This patient's bodily health is much improved and the condition of her mind clearly indicates that the above treatment has been efficacious'.

Elizabeth was discharged as cured on 7 July 1852. Her case notes recorded 'her expression was cheerful and animated and her deportment modest and respectable'. She returned to her parents' home in South Walsham where she remained until her marriage to Charles Germany at South Walsham Parish Church in January 1855.

A medical practitioner administers leeches to a patient.

When the ten-yearly census was carried out in 1861, Charles, aged 47, and Elizabeth aged 27, were living at Pilson Green, South Walsham, where Charles was employed as an agricultural labourer. Their family then included three children: James aged 7, William aged 5, and Robert aged 3. There was no sign of the child born to Elizabeth in 1851 and no birth registered that year in Elizabeth's maiden name of Westgate, so it is probable the child was stillborn. Stillborn births were not registered in the nineteenth century.

Charles and Elizabeth continued to live at the same address for the next twenty years, their family grew with another three additions: Mary Ann, Charlotte and Frederick.

Elizabeth died in 1884 and was buried on 2 March in South Walsham at the age of 50, and Charles, also buried in South Walsham, died aged 74 in 1888.

Following Elizabeth's unhappy episode at the age of eighteen, when she became mentally and physically ill after her first experience of childbirth, she married and had a family of six children, all of whom survived into adulthood. The boys remained in South Walsham as adults, married and had families of their own.

಼ೞ

At the time of Harriet Thurston's admission, in April 1867, the cause of her insanity was but one of many recorded as 'unknown'. However, her pregnancy was the supposed root of the problem, her mental disorder having begun five

weeks earlier.[13] It was reported she talked incessantly, punished her children without cause and had delusions: 'at times thinking she was a princess, or a duchess, or that a large sum of money was coming from her earnings'. Harriet was a tailoress by occupation. She had menaced her husband with a knife, threatened to throw herself out of the window, and walked about the house in a state of nudity. The mother of five children, the youngest two years of age, Harriet was expecting her sixth child within days.

After the birth of her daughter, on 4 May, she continued 'noisy, excited, swearing and very dirty in her habits' and eleven days later her baby was taken home by her sister. In July, Harriet was given digitalis as medication which quietened her for a time, but a month later she relapsed, was again noisy and excited, so the medication was discontinued. In September, she was 'wet packed', a procedure where wet sheets were wrapped around the patient at varying degrees of temperature, which was believed to have a calming effect. Initially thought to have been successful, she began employing herself with needlework on the ward. By January 1868 she was again excited, much thinner, noisy and dirty in her habits, was frequently 'dry packed' without improvement.

Four months later, at the end of May 1868, Harriet was employed in the laundry and much improved. She was now 'apparently convalescent, very industrious, talking rationally, well behaved and grateful for her mental restoration'. She was discharged, recovered, in June.

In August she was back. She had again become excited and incoherent in her conversation. Her husband, Charles, said she was in the habit of walking in the fields at night time with only her nightdress on, 'secreted knives about her person', and had developed a great dislike of her oldest daughter.

It was discovered Harriet was pregnant once more; she passed sleepless nights, sometimes out of bed gesticulating and talking in an incoherent manner, sometimes restless by day and attempting to tear her clothes.

On 12 February 1869 she 'was delivered safely and unexpectedly of a female child of diminutive size, this between 9 and 10 o'clock!' Harriet continued restless and excited, tearing her hair, and was medicated with morphia. By the end of March it was thought she had recovered from her confinement though her health was still described as feeble. On the 30 March Harriet's baby daughter was removed by the grandmother, but Harriet continued 'in a shaky condition' for the entire year of 1870, and in January 1871 had an attack of 'paralysis' that resulted in complete helplessness, being unable to dress or feed herself.

A sad end to Harriet's suffering: her death occurred in April 1871, after being treated for erysipelas, a form of cellulitis which left her unable to swallow. At about midday on the 24 April her breathing became difficult and she died in the presence of a nurse. A post mortem examination was made of the brain which was found to be 'the seat of general softening'. Cerebral softening, also known as encephalomalacia, is a localised softening of the substance of the brain, due to bleeding or inflammation.

Whilst many of the patients confined as a result of gender-specific conditions, particularly those connected with childbirth, were successfully restored to health in the asylum by the usual routine of therapeutic treatment, Harriet Thurston's case is a reminder that there were instances in this new field of medicine where the diagnosis was flawed.

Climacteric (1862-1870)

Has a meaning similar as 'change of life', implying the menopause or a time of great change.

When Maria Gidney, aged 47, entered the asylum in October 1867 she had been employed as a cook with one family in Little Walsingham for twenty-five years.[14] Maria was a single woman and had left her employer three months previously, having been unwell for a year with head pain and general debility.

Her employer in Little Walsingham was Robert Leeder, a Clerk in Holy Orders and schoolmaster, living with his wife and family of three children, plus another male teacher and a number of school boys whose ages ranged between ten and seventeen, so Maria was sometimes catering for as many as fourteen in that household. There was at least one other servant employed, but Maria was sole cook, requiring organisational ability as well as cooking skills to provide for such a large number.

It would appear that Robert and his wife Elizabeth were sympathetic to Maria when she became ill, after so many years of service in their family, and retained her services for many months until her behaviour became untenable.

Maria's history was communicated by her sister, Maryann Allwood, who thought that the climacteric period was the cause of this insanity; she explained that Maria had been very restless, unable to sleep at night, believing she was going to be killed. Her day was spent moaning and sobbing and had lately attempted to jump

The Common Place, Walsingham.

down a well.

On admission it was observed she was 'very spare' with a 'dark melancholic expression', and appeared nervous and apprehensive. After two months in the asylum she was not so restless, eating better, looking somewhat stouter and less apprehensive, but did no work.

Maria continued in a similar manner for the next three years, while her physical health improved. After another year had passed, in January 1872, it was noted that she had become most industrious in recent months with the comment: 'This also applies even to putting on her bonnet'. In July of that year William Taynton, medical officer, recorded:

> her friends having expressed a desire to try the management of the patient out of the asylum and being willing and capable of providing necessary supervision and accommodation, she was on the application of her relatives discharged this day as relieved.

Maria's sister Maryann and her husband provided a home for her in Langham where she continued to live until at least 1881. It is likely she remained with them until she died aged 66 in the summer of 1887.

ဆင္ဆ

Another patient with the diagnosis of climacteric was Jane Frost, also single, and described as a domestic servant, aged 49.[15] Jane was admitted in October 1868 when it was reported she had been ill for the past six months causing her to abandon her occupation as cook. The occupation assigned to Jane by asylum staff may have been mistaken because according to the census records in 1851 and 1871, she was on both occasions described as a tailoress. Her symptoms sound similar to those of Maria Gidney: restlessness, resisting all efforts to soothe her, headaches, and an attempt at suicide when Jane jumped from a second storey window in her night clothes, smashing several windows in her neighbour's house. A note was included to the effect that a maternal aunt had been insane, conforming to the rule that any potentially inherited traits should be identified when a patient was received into the asylum.

On admission Jane's eye and numerous parts of her body were very bruised from both her jump and her violent behaviour, and to begin with she was described as 'exceedingly troublesome constantly making the most violent attempts at escape, moreover being a strong woman she required the close attention of two nurses'. On the second day she was 'packed in wet sheets' as a calming measure, with the treatment repeated twice more before her excitement was 'subdued'.

Two months later Jane was still passing sleepless nights: 'she will not rest in bed at night time, but sits on the floor near the door with sometimes only the counterpane on her, says that she cannot breathe and that the clothes move off her in the night'.

In January 1869, after being allowed to sleep in a single room, she began to improve, was employed in the kitchen and appeared to be quite restored mentally.

Another eighteen months passed before Jane was considered fit but her discharge was delayed:

> Owing to a bilious attack, which she much exaggerated, it was deferred until another month. She complains of frequent headache which she magnifies and is always able to enter into amusements and one of the first to request to participate in any treat! She evinces no desire to return home and is too fond of her present quarters.

At the end of August 1870 Jane's discharge became a reality. She left the asylum and was finally discharged as 'recovered' at the end of October 1870, on the receipt of a satisfactory medical certificate.

Jane went to live with her brother Henry and his family when she left the asylum. Henry Frost was an ostler at an inn in King's Lynn, and Jane was listed, in the 1871 census, as Henry's unmarried sister with the occupation of tailoress.

Maria Gidney and Jane Frost, both single women of a similar age and experiencing similar symptoms, were diagnosed as climacteric within a year of each other. Maria spent four and a half years in the asylum before she was discharged as relieved and whilst Jane's symptoms were of a more violent nature than Maria's, she was discharged as recovered after three years. Both women having a much longer spell in the asylum than most of those admitted with mental disorders linked to childbirth.

Hysteria (1858-1870)

Hysteria was thought to manifest itself in women (female hysteria). It had a variety of symptoms including anxiety, shortness of breath, fainting, insomnia, irritability, nervousness, as well as, sexually forward behaviour.[16]

At this point in the mid-nineteenth century hysteria was believed to be caused by overstimulation of the mind and the treatment recommended was rest; in the case of middle-class patients this involved bed rest, a rich diet, and a temporary retirement from social activity, including reading, writing and music. For the female patients in Norfolk asylum their treatment was based on the same principle, although the reality was a pragmatic trimming of the recommendations eg. regular sleep patterns rather than constant bed rest, regular meals with additional rations—eggs or brandy, rather than 'rich' food, and regular work patterns which involved physical tasks rather than mental stimulation.

Mary Ann Goldsmith lived and worked as a domestic servant in Scarborough, Yorkshire, before having an attack of rheumatic fever a year prior to her admission in February 1869.[17] When well enough to travel, she returned home to her father in Brooke where she remained unsettled. However, in the last three months, prior to her admission in February 1869 with delusions 'that she is a lady of quality and has been robbed of her money, that she is the only daughter the Queen of England ever had, that the world is turned upside down, that she is spoilt by being drawn out and pulled to pieces etc'. It was understood she had taken a dislike to her 'stepmother' and 'threatened to chop off her head'. The identity of the person providing this history of Mary Ann's illness is not revealed in her case notes, but there is no suggestion in public records that her mother had died, nor that her father had married again; perhaps this 'stepmother' was another of Mary Ann's delusions. The cause of her mental illness was diagnosed as hysteria on her admission, although her symptoms do not appear to mirror the classic signs of that condition.

Her case notes describe her as a well behaved girl, industrious, though rather affected in her manner. After only two months she had lost her delusions and was in good health. When another two months had passed, Mary Ann was told she would be discharged at the end of the month and she 'expressed herself as being quite contented with her present abode and was not willing to leave', so was then sent 'to the worst ward where she would not be quite so comfortable'. She left the asylum, as planned, on a month's probation.

After a very short time Mary Ann returned to the asylum not having progressed satisfactorily. On this occasion her mother stated:

> soon after she had been at home her conduct became very strange. When asked to do any little needlework she would appear as if pleased at the job, but after having finished it, she would and did on several occasions undo it all again, she amused herself for a length of time together by pretending to play the piano on the table, and assumed all the airs of a lady, on one occasion she threw herself upon the floor and screamed violently, she said also that she would blow her father's brains out, had she a gun.

Once back in the asylum, Mary Ann's behaviour became quite manageable again, although she continued playing an imaginary piano and laughing in 'an imbecile manner'.

No improvement had taken place six months later in January 1870 and it was thought her delusions had returned. She continued in a similar manner for the next eight years and was still listed as a patient in the 1891 census after a period of twenty-two years.

Was her bout of rheumatic fever twenty-three years earlier the catalyst for Mary Ann's mental disorder? The timing certainly appeared to link with the onset of her breakdown in mental health. Was hysteria attributed to Mary Ann in the absence of any other detectable cause?

In 1980 hysteria was removed from the medical vocabulary as a disease in its own right, although it remains a symptom of disease, both mental and physical.[18]

Lactation (1863-1870)
Breastfeeding

Extending the period of lactation, or breastfeeding as it is more commonly known, was an early form of birth control, but for the physically frail could result in symptoms of insanity and medical superintendents were reporting a growing number of such cases in county lunatic asylums. Their experience linked the symptoms with moral issues such as poverty, physical exhaustion, malnourishment or, as they would now be termed, social problems. The term 'lactation' as a cause of insanity only came into the vocabulary of the Norfolk asylum in 1863 and Elizabeth Drake was the first patient whose symptoms were recorded as such.[19]

When Elizabeth was admitted in July 1863, she was thirty-six years old and living in Caston with her husband, a tailor, described as steady and respectable. Her condition was attributed to the fact she had been breastfeeding a two-year-old child at the same time as a baby of seven months, and had therefore become very weak. Her symptoms had been in evidence for a fortnight. In accordance with administrative regulations, it was noted that her mother and another relative were insane.

Physically, on admission, she was exhausted, very thin, with her hair cut close to her head. She was given porter daily and ¾ gram of morphine. Within a fortnight she was improving and no longer needed morphine as a sedative. Porter was considered a strengthening drink and a source of nourishment.

In mid August Elizabeth heard news of her eldest daughter's illness and this 'somewhat unsettled her'. Two and a half months after her admission, at the end of September 1863, she was discharged as recovered.

Elizabeth and Isaac, her husband, lived in Pockthorpe, Caston, with their children: Elizabeth aged 12, Charles aged 10, Benjamin aged 4, Isaac aged 2 and Emma born in January 1863. Another daughter, Mary Ann Alice, arrived in 1867.

The family continued in Pockthorpe but Isaac changed his occupation from tailor to farmer, and in 1881 he was listed as a farmer of thirty-four acres. At this date only two children remained at home: Isaac junior, at the age of 20, was a painter, and daughter, Mary Ann Alice, aged 13, was still at school.

Twenty years later, Isaac, at the age of seventy-nine, reverted to his original occupation of tailor, with eldest son Charles moving back to his parents' home to take over the farm. Isaac died on 12 February 1906 and his effects, the sum of £54 6s., passed to his son Charles, the farmer.

In 1911, Elizabeth, at the age of eighty-five, was living in the household of her son Charles, who remained unmarried, and was then described as a 'poultry dealer and killer'. Elizabeth died at the end of that year.

Charles continued his business in Caston, and both he and his mother Elizabeth were remembered by a resident who arrived in the village in 1908 at the age of fifteen:

> Charles Drake, 57, poultry dealer and killer, and a well-known character in the village, lived at Foxhall Cottage with his mother Elizabeth, 85. Perhaps someone else lived in one end of the house; certainly others lived at what I knew as outbuildings. I suspect that James Downes, boot and shoe maker, lived in one. Perhaps William 'Billy' Whitrod and Ben Drake also lived there—all three would have needed only one room down and one room up.[20]

Ben Drake, younger sibling of Charles also mentioned in this extract, was another member of the family who continued his life in Caston.

Foxhall Cottage has been converted into one dwelling, but in the early years of the twentieth century were two adjoining cottages.

Elizabeth had clearly been physically and mentally affected by her attempt to breastfeed two children at the same time but recovered during her brief spell at the asylum. Her domestic situation appeared stable and after her discharge from the asylum her life continued without any further interruption by mental illness.

Foxhall Cottage in Caston, 2020.

ಬಂಡ

Mary Ann Hanner's story was not so happily concluded: she was admitted to the asylum in July 1864, aged 30, and described as a Primitive Methodist of no education with three children. The youngest was two years old having been breastfed since birth.[21] Mary Ann had become extremely weak and stated 'that the devil tempted her to make off with her children'. She had also grasped the ten-year-old, her eldest, by the throat, and the youngest too, leaving fingermarks on the child's throat. Being constantly watched at home, she had still managed to escape the house, climb the wall and attempt to enter at another entrance believing her child was there. The whereabouts of the children during this episode was not reported. It was recorded that there was no hereditary taint, nor did the patient suffer with fits.

Her appearance on admission was noted: 'a short weakly looking woman, continually fretting about her children'. Being unable to sleep, she was given a dosage of morphia each night as a calming agent. Within a week the morphine was discontinued, Mary Ann was conversing rationally and settling to needlework by day.

At the end of November she was reported to be 'very comfortable, of great use in the ward' and working in the laundry very satisfactorily. Her mind appeared fully restored, she was very keen to return home. A month later Mary Ann was discharged as recovered.

What was not known by asylum staff were the circumstances of Mary Ann's home life. She was married in 1860 to Robert Hanner, a widower, and an agricultural labourer by occupation. Robert had a daughter, Clara born in 1854, from his first marriage. Clara was deaf from birth and unable to speak so needed more care and support than other children. Mary Ann may have found herself unable to cope with Clara's needs as well as those of her own growing family. Mary Ann gave birth to four children between 1861 and 1870, three of whom died. Eliza, died within days of her birth in 1861. Samuel died, aged 3, from mesenteric disease in 1866[22] and Maria was born in 1867. Isabella was born in 1870 and died in August 1871.

At the time of the 1871 census on 2 April, Mary Ann and Robert were living in Stow Bedon with their family of three, Clara, then aged 17, Maria aged 4 and baby daughter, Isabella, just 10 months old, who was to die four months later.

The circumstances surrounding Isabella's death were tragic. On the morning of 21 August, Robert Hanner left his home in Stow Bedon for work, leaving baby Isabella in bed with Mary Ann. Soon afterwards Maria came into the bedroom feeling unwell, so Mary Ann suggested she also get into bed with her. Moments later, taking her husband's razor she went into the second bedroom where Clara, her step-daughter was in bed, tied the girl's hands behind her back and attempted to cut her throat, inflicting serious injuries. She then returned to her own bedroom where the other two children were in bed. She seized the baby, 'nearly severing her head from her body', killing her instantly. Maria had a remarkable escape. According to newspaper reports, as Mary Ann was about to cut her throat, she pleaded, 'Oh mother please don't kill me, for I am your darling you know'. At once Mary Ann laid the razor to one side and, in her nightdress, she hurried with Maria to the nearest cottage telling her neighbour what she had done. The inquest was held on Tuesday 22 August 1871, and Mary Ann was tried for murder at the Norfolk Assizes in March 1872. She was ordered to be detained during Her Majesty's pleasure for the wilful murder of her daughter, Isabella.[23]

Mary Ann became an inmate at Broadmoor Lunatic Asylum in Berkshire

MURDER BY A LUNATIC.—At the Norfolk Assizes, before Mr Justice Blackburn, Mary Ann Hanner, a married woman, was charged with the wilful murder of her daughter, Isabella Hanner, at Stow Bedon, on the 21st of August last. It appeared that the prisoner had suffered before from mania induced by having suckled one of her children for too long a time. One of the symptoms of insanity induced by undue lactation was occasional impulses to commit murder. The prisoner, who told her neighbours that she had killed her baby immediately after she had committed the fatal act, made an attempt upon the life of another of her children, but upon the child reminding her that she was 'her little darling,' the unhappy woman desisted from her purpose. The jury found the prisoner not guilty, but she was ordered to be detained in custody during her Majesty's pleasure.

Excerpt from John O'Groats Journal, Thursday 4 April 1872.

where she spent the rest of her life. Broadmoor was initially known as Broadmoor Criminal Lunatic Asylum and the first patient admitted in 1863 was a woman convicted of infanticide. Mary Ann remained a patient in Broadmoor until her death in 1913, aged 80.

Asylum for criminal lunatics, Broadmoor, Sandhurst, Berkshire.

By 1881 the family group had dispersed. Clara was to die in Rockland All Saints workhouse in May 1873, two years after being brutally attacked by her step-mother; Robert was living in Rockland All Saints, a lodger in the household of John Cator, another farm labourer; and the only surviving child of the family, Maria, was a domestic servant in Rockland St Peter.

Parturition (1856-1870)
Childbirth, labour and delivery.

Parturition was another term used at the asylum from 1856 to describe the process of childbirth, twenty seven patients being given that diagnosis in the twenty-one years from 1851 to 1870. In 1859 Caroline Parker was admitted with this cause attributed to her condition.[24] She was aged 33 and married to a carter, living in Matlaske.

Her disorder was described as a 'case of mania' which occurred five weeks after her sixth confinement. The cause seemed to be the stoppage of her breast milk. This had the initial effect of making her restless and excited, and then frenzied and threatening, to family and friends. She was said to be 'healthy, quiet and industrious' usually, so this was quite unlike her normal conduct.

After two weeks the case book reported she had gone 'on very quietly since she arrived' and seemed beset by physical debility rather than mental ill health. Caroline was discharged at the end of December, less than a month after her admittance.

When she was re-admitted four years later, in December 1863, the cause on this occasion was described as 'due to religious matters'. Caroline was still suckling Francis, who was by then almost two years old and the youngest of her large family of eight children. This may have been a significant factor in her breakdown. The story was that her husband had 'fallen among dissenters', meaning he had joined the Nonconformists. A Methodist chapel had been built in Matlaske that year and Caroline had finally been persuaded by her husband to attend a service, although she was a member of the Church of England. Her first visit had seemed satisfactory, but on her second visit, her behaviour had been somewhat eccentric—'running in and out'. Caroline continued restless and agitated. On the morning of her admission she had become violent, breaking various household utensils and imploring that the devil be taken from her.

Caroline was described as a stout matronly woman in a very excited state, but soon calmed down and spoke quietly. She was covered with bruises and bore evident marks of rough treatment prior to her admittance. Within three weeks she was convalescent and anxious to return home. She was finally discharged in March 1864. One more son was born in Norfolk before the family moved north.

William and Caroline settled in County Durham with their growing family living in Harton, a mining village near Gateshead, when two more sons were born, completing their family of four girls and seven boys.

William was a coal miner at Harton mine when they first arrived, and in 1871 their three eldest sons were also recorded as coal miners, but William soon found work

A horse and cart near Harton Colliery, Co Durham.

which suited his skills. In Norfolk he had been a carter—driving a horse-drawn wagon to transport goods. Now he took a job as a horsekeeper.

Moving north proved beneficial for Caroline, her mental health stabilised and the family established themselves in Harton where their family remained to set up homes of their own.

୫୦୯୨

Elizabeth Desborough and her husband eventually moved north, but to Mannington in Yorkshire, some fifteen years after Elizabeth's spell in the asylum.[25] In January 1858, Elizabeth, née Marston, and John Desborough were living in Wiggenhall St Germans, five miles south-west of King's Lynn, when Elizabeth gave birth to her first child, a daughter named Mary. It was thought she went out too soon after her confinement and 'in her excitement committed a petty theft'. When arrested it was immediately thought she was of 'unsound mind' and sent to the asylum. Parturition was diagnosed as the cause of her disorder, and fomentation recommended for her painful breasts. A month later her breasts were better and her appetite had improved, but she was still shouting and singing constantly, and 'destructive to her clothing day and night'.

After five months she was reported to be very well and anxious to see her husband and child. In June, she began fretting as she had not seen or heard from her husband since her admission, so was discharged, initially on trial, and in July was confirmed as recovered.

When the 1861 census was taken, Elizabeth and John were living at Wiggenhall St Germans in the household of John's mother, a widow, with his brother, his unmarried sister and a grandchild, as well as their own daughter Mary, aged 3, and their twin baby girls, Elizabeth and Maria, just nine months old.

Ten years later at the time of the 1871 census, Elizabeth and John had moved into their own accommodation in Tilney cum Islington, approximately one mile from Wiggenhall St Germans. Their family then included four daughters, Louisa was born in 1864, but twin boys, Isaac and John, born in 1862, had both died as infants. Two daughters, Mary and Maria, aged 13 and 10 respectively, were both employed as agricultural labourers, alongside their father.

By 1881 Elizabeth and John had moved away from Norfolk and were settled in Manningham, a suburb of Bradford in Yorkshire. They were living at 27 Girlington Road and their household included daughters, Mary, Maria, Louisa and Sabrina born in 1872. Daughter Elizabeth had married Charles March in 1880 and the newly weds were also living with Elizabeth and John. Manningham was a mill town and the daughters were employed as wool combers and worsted spinners. The move north had afforded them better work prospects than Norfolk, where they had been toiling in the fields at ten years old and exposed to the elements in all seasons.

Twenty years later, Elizabeth and John were still living at the same address with just one daughter, Mary, whose birth had been the catalyst for Elizabeth's one and only spell in the asylum. Her sister Pamela was less fortunate, and her story is told in a later case study (see p. 58ff) .

ഇറാൻ

Another patient whose mental ill health was assigned to parturition, or the birth of her child, was Emma Tice, aged 27, who was described as a washerwoman when she was admitted to the asylum in May 1861.[26] She was married and living in Aldborough with her husband, Robert, and contributing to the family income by her work. At that time she was described as a tall, slight woman with a lymphatic temperament. A surprising assessment since Emma's condition was recorded as 'mania' and the term 'lymphatic' implies a lack of energy. Other physical features were noted: head hot; skin dry; pulse quick; tongue furred; bowels confined; but no epilepsy. Her head was described as 'small and narrow and high at apex', the last comment relevant in view of the Victorian preoccupation with phrenology.

It was noted that Emma did well in the days following the birth of her first child, but the baby died and she became restless, feverish and delirious, and was removed to the asylum in a feeble condition. On arrival she was prescribed an aperient and a sedative, the aperient to relieve her constipation and the sedative to calm her.

She remained delirious for three weeks and often required sedatives during that time. She was given porter daily and at the end of three weeks her appetite had improved, she was reasonably tranquil and had begun to do a little needlework. Emma suffered a series of relapses until August when she stabilised, and in September, it was reported she had needed quinine for neuralgia but, apart from that, she was then in good health. She was discharged as having recovered in October 1861 with the comment, 'has got quite fat and left recovered today'.

Emma Ayres and Robert Tice were married in June 1860 in the parish church of Thurgarton. Robert was born in Aldborough, Norfolk, but Emma originated from London, Grays Inn Lane in the parish of Holburn. In 1851 she was still living in London, working as a servant at Berners Street, Marylebone, in the household of an artist, Robert Hume.[27] Berners Street at that time was 'celebrated as the home and haunt of artists, painters and sculptors' so Emma's situation as a domestic servant employed at a good address and working for a middle-class household would seem an enviable one, but it was not enough to keep her in London. Emma moved to Norfolk at some stage in the 1850s, though the reason for her move is not known.

In 1861 Emma and Robert, an agricultural labourer, were living in Aldborough awaiting the birth of their first child. After the birth and subsequent death of the child, Emma spent six months in the asylum until her recovery. In the following ten years Emma gave birth to four sons, Walter, Arthur, Robert and Harry, with just one brief re-admission for three months in 1866. Living just four doors away from Emma and Robert on The Green, Aldborough, were Robert's sibling William and his young family.

Photographs of patients first appeared in the case books in 1873, and Emma's was taken at her re-admission in 1877 when she was forty-four years old.

Aldborough Green.

In June 1878 Emma went into the asylum with anxiety caused by nursing her husband Robert, who was to die on 28 July, aged 58, whilst Emma was still a patient. She was discharged in October but, in February 1879, was re-admitted once again. This time the cause of her mental breakdown was described as poverty. She remained until July 1881, when she was once more discharged as recovered. During Emma's stay in the asylum her four sons were living with Thomas Tice, Robert's nephew, and his family in Thurgarton, just half a mile from Aldborough. Thomas, also an agricultural labourer, and his wife, Ann, had five children of their own, so providing a home for Robert's

Emma Tice in 1877 aged 44 (Norfolk Record Office SAH267).

family of four boys, created a crowded household. Emma was re-admitted once again in December 1885, now aged 52 and a widow living in Thurgarton, she is described as being in feeble health. she was discharged in June 1887 having recovered once more. Her final admission came in February 1890 where she was described as housekeeper to her sons in Aldborough, aged 56, and suffering with recurrent mania having received no relief from the parish. She remained a patient in the asylum from 1890 until her death on 6 June 1894.

Was Robert the support that kept Emma's mental illness at bay during the years between her first mental illness and her breakdown at the time of Robert's final illness? Was the added stress of Robert's death the catalyst for Emma's final descent into insanity? We can only speculate.

‟)(⁗

Susannah Phillippo was admitted to the asylum five years after her marriage in 1865 to James Phillippo, at which time Susannah and James were living in Foulsham with their two boys, one aged seven and the other aged six months; a third child, a daughter, born in 1867 had died early in 1868 only a few months old.[28]

Prior to this attack Susannah was reported to have been low-spirited on account of the death of her daughter. Just three days before her admittance, in

April 1870, she became 'violent, noisy, incoherent and raving', rejecting food that was offered and destroying furniture and clothing. Two days later she seized her sister by the throat, injury only being averted by the intervention of a third party.

On admission she was considered to be in feeble health but free from bruises, thus confirming no physical ill-treatment or injury had occurred before her reception into the asylum. In the first two days as a patient Susannah had spells of violence so great three nurses were needed to restrain her—she was 'packed' to calm her on successive days. Susannah continued to be unmanageable and was given chloral which sometimes quietened her, however, there were still occasions when she made sudden and violent attacks upon the nurses. She was 'packed' at intervals, given chloral doses at other times, both of which produced temporary relief. This pattern continued for a year until in March 1871 she was 'blistered'. Blistering was a treatment considered effective at that time in which a powder was applied to the skin made from blister beetles with the possible addition of pepper, or mustard seed. It resulted in a blister forming on the skin. When the blister burst, it was believed, the toxin causing the disorder would be expelled from the patient's body. A blister was created on the back of Susannah's neck in March and, in April, it was reported that her natural state of mind had returned. She conversed rationally and was free from all excitement, so the treatment was considered a success.

At the end of June, Susannah was discharged as recovered. Remaining in good health for sixteen months, she was re-admitted in October 1872 after a relapse that had occurred several weeks earlier. She had complained of severe headaches, lost her appetite and gradually became weaker until she was unable to attend to her domestic duties. Two weeks later, she began talking strangely, moving furniture for no purpose and 'peering into her neighbours' pantry'. Susannah's neighbour reported her memory was much impaired and attributed the cause of her current attack to ill health. On examination the thirty-seven years old behaved 'like a young hysterical girl'.

Throughout 1873, a similar pattern of behaviour to her earlier admission to the asylum was displayed, but, by October 1874, she had greatly improved being discharged as recovered in November 1874. James remained in Foulsham and in 1871, when Susannah was having treatment in the asylum, his sister Mary acted as housekeeper for him, looking after the two boys, and allowing James to continue work as a fowl dealer.

Susannah was taken into the asylum for the sixth time in October 1878 when she was forty years old. She had continued well since her last discharge in 1874, but now weighed 8 st. 8 lb. This relapse began with restlessness and progressed to an inability to attend to her household affairs. Her condition deteriorated. She talked incessantly and incoherently, was continually excited, 'using blasphemous and filthy language and tearing everything she can lay her hands upon, and is very violent'. These symptoms continued, with only short periods of improvement, until, in May 1882, she was considered to have recovered and was discharged. She weighed 9 st. 4 lb.—an increase of ten pounds.

At the time of the 1881 census, James Phillippo was living in the village of Gateley. Susannah, although being listed at the family home and described

Susannah Phillippo in 1878 aged 40 (Norfolk Record Office SAH268).

as a 'lunatic', had, in fact, been re-admitted to the asylum in October 1878 and would not have been at home in 1881.

James and his family moved to Worthing, Norfolk, in 1881 or 1882 evidenced by the 1883 edition of *William White's History, Gazeteer and Directory of Norfolk*. It lists among its principal residents, James Phillippo, fellmonger and skin dresser of Worthing tanyard.

In 1891 James and Susannah were still living in Worthing with their son James, named as an assistant

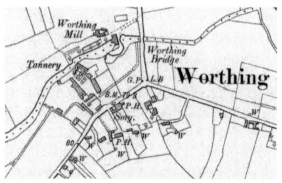

1905 Ordnance Survey map showing the tannery at Worthing.

Norwich Union Insurance Company employees visiting Worthing tannery in September 1894.

to his father. In the household was a niece aged 15, providing support to the family and to Susannah. James senior died in November 1897 leaving a legacy of £3,281 to his son James and John Frederick Bone, wheelwright and builder.

James senior had made a success of his business. A surviving photograph shows Norwich Union Insurance Company employees visited the tannery in September 1894. The man standing on the extreme right is thought to be James Phillippo.

Writing in the 1930s, the process of 'fellmongering' in Worthing was described by Norman Lowe, whose father worked at the tannery:

Sheepskins were collected from various slaughter houses around Norfolk. The skins were then sorted and placed in soaking pits. These pits were formed in the fellmongering shed from a stream diverted from the river Blackwater and then on to join the river again at Worthing bridge. After the skins were soaked to make them more pliable they were dragged out with some cromes and placed on trimming beams, the fellmonger then used a very sharp two handled knife to remove all surplus fat and the front leg bones.

The skins were then folded ready to go into the paint shop where they were spread out on a very large table, the inside of the skin facing upwards and then painted with this very strong chemical. The workers had to wear long-armed rubber gloves and aprons. The skins were then placed on solid concrete racks for at least 24 hours, allowing the chemical to work to release the wool. The skins were then loaded on to small trucks that ran on a small gauge rail track connecting the fellmonger shed with the wool pulling shed.

James Phillippo junior inherited the tannery when his father died, with disastrous results, for the business did not thrive under his management. He was repeatedly summonsed for drunkenness in the years following the death of his father. Did he find the responsibility of the tannery a burden? Was it a source of unbearable stress and anxiety? It was reported in the *Norfolk News* in 1900 that he was summoned to the Dereham Petty Sessions in breach of the Public Health Act 1875 when material from the tannery had been polluting the local water supply. James agreed to the recommendations of the Medical Officer of Health and the case was adjourned for twelve months. The tannery was eventually sold, in 1906, when James was thirty-seven years old, still a relatively young man. Whether Susannah's or James junior's mental health was affected by exposure to the tanning process is a moot point. It has been suggested, in recent years, that tannery workers were at risk of both physical and mental health problems caused by the chemicals used in the process.[29]

In 1901, Susannah was once more a patient in the asylum and remained there until she died in 1910. Once James senior died, Susannah no longer had the assistance she needed to remain at home. He had supported her for many years and, with his passing, she had no recourse but to return to the asylum. She was buried at Worthing Church in December 1910.

∞)(∞

Sarah Murgett (sometimes written as Murgate) had been a patient two years prior to her admission, in May 1869, with the cause attributed to parturition.[30] In 1867, following the birth of her fourth child, she had been admitted with accouchement. She spent four months in the asylum before being assessed as recovered and therefore discharged.

Between her discharge in December 1867 and her re-admission in May 1869, Sarah had a miscarriage, then, subsequently, another confinement on 9 March 1869, after which she 'began to complain of pain in her head and became very low spirited being afraid that she was going to lose her reason for the second time'. It was noted she became restless and unable to care for herself or her infant. She threatened to kill her husband, her children and cut her own throat.

Harsh treatment by her husband was noted, though parturition was recorded as the cause of her attack. A few days after being admitted Sarah was suffering with a swollen face said to be the result of cold. By the end of June, she had recovered and appeared in good health—'was clean, cheerful and very industrious'. After a further two months in the same 'satisfactory condition of mind and body' Sarah was discharged, cured, at the end of August 1869.

Domestic female activities such as sewing were encouraged as 'voluntary labour' to distract and 'normalise' a woman's condition in asylums. In J. Trayer's 'Sewing workshop', 1854, we see the idealised version of such pursuits.

Sarah and Henry had married in the spring of 1861 and just a few weeks later, in April of that year, the couple were living with Henry's parents in Hanworth. Henry was a shoemaker and Sarah a dressmaker. Ten years later, during which time Sarah had twice been a patient in the asylum, Sarah and Henry, with their family of six, were still living with Sarah's widowed father. Henry's occupation was listed as postman.

Another ten years saw Sarah and Henry living separately from their in-laws. By this time their family was complete. Ten children between the ages of nineteen and one year all living at home with their parents. The couple were recorded in their original occupations—Henry as a shoemaker and Sarah a milliner. The 1911 census shows that they remained in Hanworth maintaining the same occupations. Sarah died in 1916.

Did Sarah's mental health break down due to the pressures of sharing a household with her husband's parents? She had no further periods of mental disorder recorded once the family had their own home.

Puerperal (1857-1870)

A fever occurring soon after childbirth and much feared in the nineteenth century. In the majority of patients the disease appeared on the third day, and commenced with rigour, headache and the "cold fit" followed by extreme heat, perspiration and thirst. Abdominal pain was an almost ubiquitous feature and this began as a mild symptom, becoming increasingly severe over the duration of the disease and often resulting in fatality.[31] The term 'puerperal' in itself indicates the six week period post-parturition and the majority of the cases recorded at NLA were puerperal insanity rather than puerperal fever.

Puerperal insanity should not be confused with the life-threatening puerperal fever. It was a condition that developed in women before, during or after the process of childbirth and had a multiplicity of associated symptoms: sleeplessness, rapid pulse, pallor or flushed skin, vivid eyes, furred tongue, constipation, delirium, excitability and delusions. Triggered by the dangerous process of childbirth, puerperal insanity included pregnancy and lactational insanity.

This condition was first recorded at the asylum in 1857 and experienced by at least twenty-one women during the twenty year period 1851 to 1870. The condition arose sometimes during pregnancy, and often within a very short period following childbirth and manifested itself either in melancholia or in mania.

Fanny Craven, aged 25, a schoolmistress, was admitted in January 1864 apparently suffering from an attack of mania which had begun three weeks after giving birth some months previously.[32] It was noted she was always worse during her menstrual period. Her husband described her behaviour as follows:

At the commencement of an attack she laughs very much and

Physiognomy of mental diseases by Morison, Alexander, 1779-1866.

knowing that I do not like to see it she will attempt to explain by saying she was thinking of something amusing. She soon ceases to give this explanation and her laughing fit becomes more frequent and more immodest. She then begins to find fault without cause and gets wrong notions into her head which cause her to become very excited.

Royal Arms on the portico of the school at Flitcham, Norfolk.

On admission she was recorded as a thin, spare, short respectable looking woman in a very excited state, talking incessantly. Within a month Fanny had improved and thought it cruel of her husband to let her remain in 'such company'. After less than four months she was discharged and returned to her family.

Robert, Fanny's husband, was a schoolmaster born in Yorkshire, and in August 1863 they were living in Bacton, Norfolk. Their family eventually increased to seven: Julia, John Carpenter, Robert Lound, Fanny Alexandra, Ellen Amelia, Mabel and Susan.

Robert and Fanny married in Norfolk in 1859, their first child, Julia, was born in Norfolk, their second, John, when they were resident in Bedfordshire. They returned to Norfolk in 1863 and Robert Lound, Fanny Alexandra and Ellen Amelia were all born in the county, but by 1870 they had moved to Beckley in Oxfordshire, where Mabel arrived, and a year later, in 1872, their last born, Susan, was welcomed at Stillington in Yorkshire, Robert's home county. By 1881 they were back in Norfolk living at Terrington St John, and in 1891 at Flitcham, where Robert was the village schoolmaster.

Robert and Fanny moved at least eight times during their married life, Robert a schoolmaster throughout those years. The reasons for so

The Ship, Brancaster.

many moves remains a mystery, but constant re-location meant an unsettling lifestyle for the children. Julia, their firstborn, had moved in with her maternal grandmother, Ann Carpenter, by the age of eleven in 1871; Ann, a widow, was then an innkeeper running the *Ship Inn* at Brancaster.

Ten years later, siblings Robert Lound and Ellen Amelia had joined their grandmother and sister in South Everard Street, King's Lynn, where Ann and Julia were then living, next to Fanny's brother, Frederick Carpenter, a brewer.

Robert and Fanny moved again in the 1890s to London and were living in Agamemnon Road, Hampstead, where Robert died in May 1897. Probate was granted to John Carpenter Craven, their eldest son, a telegraphist by occupation, the value of Robert's effects was £98 13s. 6d.

Fanny remained in Hampstead after Robert died, living at Burrard Road with her two younger daughters, Mabel and Susan, both single, and Susan a dressmaker by trade. In 1911, Fanny was living in the household of her eldest daughter, Julia, together with Mabel and Susan, at Achilles Road, Hampstead.

Fanny and Robert enjoyed a seemingly peripatetic lifestyle throughout their married life, without any apparent adverse affects on Fanny's mental health after the one occasion which required treatment within the asylum. Fanny died in Hampstead in 1912 at the age of seventy-three, leaving no will.

∞◊◊

When Charlotte Royle, aged 37, the wife of the rector of Bittering, was admitted in June 1861 it was perceived she was suffering from a recurrent bout of puerperal mania, which had lasted eight days.[33] It was recorded that there was 'a strong hereditary taint of mental disease' which had caused her to have several previous bouts of mental disorder.

She was the daughter of the rector of Necton, and had an older brother, John Collett Reynolds, who entered the Church and became rector of Beeston St Andrew, and subsequently rector of Holton, Suffolk from 1845 to 1855. The Rev John Reynolds sadly died at Higham Hall private asylum in August 1855, at the age of 34, giving credence to the initial intimation of mental illness within the family.

An observation about her physical demeanour was made on admittance: 'Spare habit of body and sanguine temperament. Head long and narrow. Countenance flushed and excited. Tongue furred. Bowels confined. Skin hot. Viscera seem healthy—no epilepsy.' These were familiar observations referring to visual appearance frequently recorded in patients' case notes and considered an important factor in determining personality. Epilepsy, at that time untreatable, was therefore important to establish from the outset.

On this occasion Charlotte was transferred to Norfolk asylum from the Bethel Hospital in Norwich, and was prescribed extra diet which included two ounces of port, and porter daily, also an aperient to relieve her constipation.

When Charlotte became ill in 1861 she was living at the Old Farm House in Little Bittering with her husband, James, who was rector of the village. Charlotte's situation was not one of dire poverty, but was precipitated by puerperal insanity following recent childbirth. She and James had four children: James junior aged 8, Elizabeth aged 6, Laura aged 4, and the youngest Amelia, born in March of that year, plus a nursemaid, a cook and a nurse in the household.

After her first month in the asylum Charlotte's restlessness improved, she became quieter 'in a sullen and obstinate way'. During the following two months her condition remained the same until, in September, it was noted she began to converse, and expressed a desire to go home. She was discharged on 24 September and, in November, it was recorded that she was much better. Charlotte had another breakdown attributed to puerperal insanity in 1863 when she spent just one week in the asylum, although it was probably a stillbirth as no child was registered at that time.

By 1871 Charlotte and James had moved from Little Bittering and were living with their four children and just one servant in Church Street, Litcham, though James was still rector of Bittering. It seems possible this move was due to financial constraints, the population of Little Bittering was small amounting

St Peter and St Paul Church, Bittering, Norfolk.

to thirty residents, and the annual income of the rector was correspondingly modest.

James died in 1879, aged 69, and two years later Charlotte was living in Cathedral Close, Norwich, with her youngest daughter, Amelia. Charlotte died in 1888 aged 65.

Despite the warnings of 'a strong hereditary trait' of mental illness when Charlotte was admitted to the asylum, there was no evidence of a recurrence after 1863. So Charlotte enjoyed twenty-five years during which she was apparently free from mental illness.

෧෬

Another patient admitted to the asylum with puerperal insanity was Pamela Herring, aged 29, the wife of a labourer living at Cley-next-the-Sea, and the mother of eight children in 1866; these and the following details were provided by a neighbour on her entry to the asylum.[34] A month previous she had given birth to a stillborn child, after a very debilitating labour lasting four days. She had become excited soon after, muttering to herself and sometimes refusing food; her condition had worsened in the past three days and she had become destructive, mischievous, using foul language and rampaging about her home at night. Just the day before her admission she had attempted to throw herself into a pond. It was noted she was rambling in her speech saying 'she had been delivered of three children, that she is the mother of twenty-five children, that she is God Almighty ...'. It was noted that her mother and aunt had been insane. Her sister Elizabeth had a breakdown following the birth of her first child and is the subject of an earlier case study (see p. 45ff). About eight years prior to her admission with puerperal mania Pamela had been a patient at the asylum.

It was noted that, on admission, she was very thin and in delicate health. She was also very dirty, her clothes and body covered with vermin. She was prescribed porter daily as an additional source of nourishment.

For the first month Pamela continued to be noisy, abusive, violent and restless at night. She was prescribed morphia to calm her. After a month it was reported that she was quieter at night, looking better, and had gained weight. There was very little change in her behaviour recorded until June 1867 when she was transferred to a different ward. Although she appeared to settle and to work, she needed watching as was still apt to be 'mischievous'. After eighteen months in the asylum Pamela's mental state remained stable and she had gained weight. By May 1868 she was more active and, having expressed a desire to return home, the medical superintendent thought it reasonable to recommend a month's trial in her domestic situation. The month was completed satisfactorily and Pamela was discharged in June 1868, almost two years after her admission.

Pamela Herring in 1887 aged 52 (Norfolk Record Office SAH285).

At the beginning of the year 1851 Pamela Marston, born in Ireland, was sixteen years old and living with her parents, Samuel and Naomi Marston in Wiveton, a small village, nine miles from Holt. At that time Robert Herring, aged 24, was temporarily in the Holt workhouse with his father, William, and four siblings. Pamela and

Robert married towards the end of 1851 and two years later, at the baptism of their daughter Eliza, they were living in Cley-next-the-Sea where they were to remain for all their married lives. In 1861, their family had grown to include three daughters, Eliza, Phoebe and Harriet, but there had been at least one sad loss in those years—Mary Ann, born in 1858, had died the following year. This was the time of Pamela's first sojourn at the asylum, from November 1858 to October 1859. Mary Ann was just a few months old when Pamela was admitted in November 1858 and died while her mother was still being treated in the asylum.

When Pamela was admitted to the asylum again in 1866, she was recorded as the mother of eight children: another daughter, Sarah Ann, had been born in 1862. The child born in 1866 was stillborn, making a total of six births. Perhaps the neighbour providing Pamela's history was mistaken, or, there had been two more stillbirths of which they were unaware. There had been another death in 1863 when Harriet, born 1860, had died.

Twins arrived in 1869, Minnie and Rosanna, who proved the catalyst for Pamela's third admission to the asylum. She spent two months there, from April to June 1869, after the twins' birth. Both died as infants, Rosanna in 1870 and Minnie in 1871.

A fourth admission was recorded in 1871 when Pamela returned yet again. Was this the result of a stillbirth or miscarriage? No birth was registered giving Robert and Pamela Herring as parents at that time. In 1871, while Pamela was in the asylum, Robert was residing in the Erpingham Union workhouse, West Beckham, with two of their three surviving daughters, Elizabeth, aged 18, and Sarah Ann, aged 8. Their third daughter, Phoebe, was working in domestic service at the *Queen Adelaide*, an inn in Holt, a distance of approximately four miles from her father and sisters in West Beckham.

By 1881 Robert and Pamela were reunited and living together at Sturges Yard, Cley, with daughter, Phoebe and her three children, Eliza and Louisa, aged 7 and 4 years, and John aged 11 months. Robert was still working as a general labourer at the time.

Robert died in 1885 and in 1891

Sturges Yard, Cley in 2020.

In 1911 Walter James Gaze was still in Gimingham, a widower aged 57, continuing his lifelong occupation as a miller. Living with him was his daughter Lucy, aged 27, acting as housekeeper, also son Walter, aged 24, a miller like his father, plus younger daughter May (Mary), aged 22, with no occupation assigned to her. At that time the family were living comfortably in a property with eight rooms.

These glimpses of Eliza's life, through the censuses taken at ten-yearly intervals, indicate she went on to live a full and fruitful life after her initial breakdown and spell within the asylum.

These case studies were chosen to give a fuller picture of the types of mental breakdown experienced by female patients attributed to gender-specific causes that were treated at Norfolk asylum during the years 1851 to 1870. Many more female patients were researched, but after discharge from the asylum, these ex-patients' lives were not found in public records and therefore disappear from view.

Ten of the fifteen gender-specific causes of insanity are exemplified in these cases studies. Thirteen patients recovered and appeared to resume their normal lives without further interludes of mental illness. Of the remaining eight, two died in the asylum from physical illness, one committed suicide whilst a patient, one remained in the asylum for another twenty-three years and was assumed to have eventually died there and another was sent to Broadmoor Criminal Lunatic Asylum and died in that institution. Finally, three of the women had numerous re-admissions. It is particularly noticeable that their symptoms escalated following the death of their husbands, who presumably provided enough stability and support when their wives recovered sufficiently to be discharged. Once their husbands died that safety net disappeared, their re-admissions becoming more frequent and prolonged, until they died as patients of the asylum.

Notes

1   E. Showalter, *The Female Malady: Women, Madness, and English Culture, 1830-1980* (London, 1985), p. 55

2   Charlotte Perkins Gilmore, *The Yellow Wallpaper* (London, 2009), p. 4

3   Norfolk Record Office SAH 263 (Female Case Book August 1861-December 1865)

4   Norfolk Record Office SAH 264 (Female Case Book December 1865-April 1870)

5   https://scotlandspeople.gov.uk (accessed February 2020)

6   Ibid 4

7   Ibid

8   Dersingham History Website accessed April 2020

9   Norfolk Record Office SAH 262 (Female Case Book March 1853-August 1861)

10   Ibid.

11   Norfolk Record Office SAH 260 (Case Book December 1848-April 1853)

12   https://www.Britannica.com/science/leeching (accessed May 2020)

13   Ibid 4

14   Ibid

15   Ibid

16   https://en.wikipedia.org/wiki/Hysteria (accessed March 2020)

17   Ibid 4

18   https://wellcomecollection.org/articles/W89GZBIAAN4yz1hQ (accessed May 2020)

19   Ibid 3

20   https://www.caston-online.co.uk/acastonwalk1911.asp (accessed April 2020)

21   Ibid 3

22   Mesenteric disease: a condition that more often affects children and teenagers which causes inflammation and swelling in the lymph nodes inside the abdomen. https://www.healthline.com

23   *Norfolk Chronicle and Norwich Gazette*, 26 August, 1871

24   Ibid 9

25   Ibid

26   Ibid

27   Edward Walford, *Old and New London Volume 4* (1878) via https://www.british-history.ac.uk/old-new-london/vol4 (accessed June 2020)

28   Norfolk Record Office SAH 265 (Case Book April 1870-June 1874)

29   J Maurice, *Bulletin of the World Health Organization*, 2001 (SciELO Public Health)

30   Ibid 4

31   https://www.ncbi.nlm.nih.gov/pmc/articles/PMC1088248/ (accessed March 2020)

32   Ibid 9

33   Ibid

34   Ibid 4

35   Ibid

36   Surrey Marriage Bonds and Allegations records held by the London Metropolitan Archives (accessed via Ancestry February 2020)

37   *England & Wales, National Probate Calendar (Index of Wills and Administrations), 1858-1995* (accessed February 2020)

Happy Arcadia by Konstantin Makovsky, 1889-90.

Leaving the Asylum

THE ethos of asylum provision was one of treatment and cure. It was intended that patients would receive treatment that would result in their recovery and consequent discharge, and so enable them to return to their former lives, stronger both physically and mentally. Arcadia was perhaps beyond the hopes of the most optimistic supporters of the asylum system although there was a conviction amongst alienists that early treatment would result in a cure. There were 2,332 admissions between 1851 and 1870 and of those 1,051 patients had been discharged, amounting to 45 percent, 930 of whom had been considered cured, the remaining 121 'relieved', so although not cured were improved enough to return to the community.

Officially there were two ways in which patients were released from Norfolk Lunatic Asylum. The first was by the recommendation of the superintendent who was legally obliged[1], when patients were recovered, to give notice to the Committee of Visitors who would arrange for their discharge within 14 days. The second, by the application of friends or relatives for the release of the patient— most frequently the spouse or parent of the patient—having a close familial tie.

Norfolk was one of the first county lunatic asylums to differentiate between patients who had been discharged and those who had recovered.[2] Patients' recovery was assessed on their ability to participate in the day-to-day activities of the asylum, 'by responsible conduct, rational communication, willingness to labour, and participation in recreational tasks considered appropriate'. Hence the frequent references to patients' industriousness in their case notes. From the early 1850s, the case books at the asylum recorded the progress of patients in detail and tracked their headway towards discharge. A system of probationary discharge was introduced in 1855, which allowed 'probationers' a gradual return to independence with grants provided for those whose health prevented hard physical work. In this chapter we continue to focus on female patients.

We met Susanna Sargeant (see p. 20ff), a governess by occupation, when she was admitted in February 1870. By the end of March her case notes recorded she was 'decidedly improved, being more natural in conversation and behaviour, obedient and inclined to be industrious and tidily in habits'. Four months later she was making a significant contribution to life within the asylum by playing the harmonium on Sundays and leading the singing in chapel. In September it was decided she should be sent out on a month's probation which was satisfactorily completed and six months later, in 1871, she was employed as an assistant teacher at a school in Banham.

Rachael Cutting, a widow with one child aged 8, was living in Broome with her parents on her admission in September 1868.[3] She had been earning four shillings and sixpence a week (£14.09) to maintain herself and her child and, had reputedly received harsh treatment from her mother and father. Her case notes present a sad picture, 'her failing bodily health, the unkind treatment from her parents, her great anxiety on her child's account and the dread of starvation seems to have caused her mind to give way'. Initially she was prescribed morphia as a calming agent. This was discontinued after only two weeks and she soon improved to work 'industriously' in the laundry. After a mere two months Rachael was discharged 'cured'.[4] Both patients recovered within a short space of time supporting the view that early diagnosis and a therapeutic regime rendered a successful outcome.

The second method of discharge from the asylum was at the request of patients' kin. The medical superintendent made recommendations to the Committee of Visitors in each case with due consideration to the domestic circumstances of each patient. In one instance, William Hills, the medical superintendent, seems eventually to have given permission against his better judgement. In December 1869, Mary Ann Stowers' husband, a merchant, 'who is permitted to visit her, frequently brings a quantity of provisions with him about every other day, consisting of every description of game, wine, brandy etc.' applied for permission to take Mary Ann home, but William Hills recorded that 'her health is much impaired, it is scarcely possible that she can receive the necessary care and attention at her home as she does here.' Mr Stowers' request was rejected because, on 28 March 1870, another note was recorded in the superintendent's report book that Mary Ann's husband intended to apply once again for her return home with the comment: 'altho her health is much better her mental state is very unsatisfactory and her case hopeless.' Despite the obvious reluctance on the part of the superintendent, it seems that permission was granted on this occasion. On 1 April a further entry appeared: 'Mary Stowers was brought back having been out only 3 days—the husband found (as I had warned him) that he could exercise no control over her and was thankful to be relieved of the responsibility.'

Despite these difficulties, Mary Ann was eventually discharged as 'relieved' in June 1870, appearing 'better in mind and body than she has ever been before', indicating that her mental illness had a cause other than the general paralysis which had been diagnosed on her admission.

Another request more positively received came from Eunice Tovell's parents.[5] She was admitted in December 1862, a schoolmistress aged 45, who had been subject to periods of mental disorder for twenty-six years. She had been cared for at home, except for six months in the Bethel Hospital, Norwich. After four years in the asylum William Hills recorded in May 1866, 'Eunice's parents are very aged and express a great wish that she should meet them and her sister at Alpington, to spend a week with other relatives there.'[6] He noted she was tranquil at the time and requested permission of the Committee to grant the request, making the point that 'it is a privilege frequently allowed in other asylums.'

On 10 July 1866 another entry recorded:

Eunice Tovell returned after passing 10 days with her relatives at Alpington, they were gratified by the indulgence extended and the patient much pleased with the holiday.

The Tovell family were of some substance in the village, their name having been adopted as an official address, Tovell's Corner. John Tovell, Eunice's father had been a wheelwright in 1851 and Tovell's Corner was recorded on the census returns of Alpington between 1851 and 1901.[7] Eunice was one of four sisters, all schoolmistresses and all single women. After her eventual discharge from the asylum, she made her home with her sisters, firstly in Suffolk and then in Essex.

Ordnance Survey map of Alpington, 1905. Markers show possible location of Tovell's Corner.

Only one admission during the twenty years under review was recorded with the cause 'over mental exertion', a symptom often attributed to middle-class women suffering with postnatal depression but, on this occasion, attributed to Elizabeth Fisher, a young single woman employed as a governess in a small girls' school. She was described as a small, delicately made girl with a great curvature of the spine; she complained of great pain in her spine, which was becoming more distorted. As a result she was reluctant to lie down, and could only manage to recline on a couch. Elizabeth gradually improved over the course of a year, enjoying the fortnightly balls, voluntarily reading aloud to the patients and writing affectionate letters to her family. Her brother, who was in comfortable circumstances, applied to take her home and Elizabeth was discharged relieved after fifteen months in the asylum. It seems likely that Elizabeth's mental disorder was as much due to her physical condition as to mental incapacity.

The response of the medical superintendent in these applications indicates a familiarity with the condition of the patients concerned, and an understanding of what would be in their best interests.

There were other less orthodox methods of exiting the asylum, one being that of escape. While there were numerous attempts at escape documented regularly in the medical superintendent's monthly report, most of these attempts were thwarted at an early stage and only a very few were successful. One female patient escaped in November 1868 and was away for just one night: Maria Freestone had been admitted the previous month, aged 23 and single, she had a child of six months old and declared she went to see the child.[8] Maria remained in the asylum until she died five years later from phthisis.

Another irregular route out of the asylum was that of suicide, a significant criminal act in the mid-Victorian era. It was only with the Suicide Act 1961 that it ceased to be a crime. Suicide might result in the verdict *felo de se* or self-murder, a crime which was punishable by forfeiture of property and, until 1823, potentially denied those that were successful the right to be buried in consecrated ground. Many patients were recorded as having suicidal tendencies on their admission, although relatively few exhibited signs of self-harm after being admitted.

Charlotte Ringwood is an example of a woman who attempted suicide. A servant at the age of thirteen, she had been subjected to physical abuse when she 'had been seduced' by her employer, which would now be considered statutory rape, and experienced two pregnancies as a consequence. She was then 'befriended' by another man whom she married, and subsequently suffered ill treatment from him, specifically a lack of food and inadequate clothing. Charlotte threatened suicide and attempted to carry out her threat. The second night after her admission, in April 1865, she attempted suicide by strangulation, tearing a handkerchief which she tied tightly round her neck. The night staff on their rounds were attracted by her peculiar breathing, and removed the handkerchief from her throat where it had left a deep red wound on her neck. As a result of this attempt, she was placed 'in the padded room, to sleep in strong clothes and be carefully watched by day.'

After four months it was noted Charlotte was working well and willingly in the laundry; she seemed comfortable mentally, her general health was very good and she was discharged at the end of August 1865. None of the patients who attempted suicide whilst in the asylum, and failed, were prosecuted. Instead they were given extra attention and placed in as safe an environment as possible.

Lucy English was admitted in May 1850 suffering from melancholia. She had 'manifested a strong suicidal tendency having attempted strangulation by means of her apron strings' on 15 June.[9] In view of this serious attempt Lucy was put into the padded room and visited 'at short intervals by the attendant.' At ten o'clock that evening it was reported that she had inflicted a wound to her body:

> under the influence of imaginary demoniacal possession, [she] lay on the left side with the transverse colon and all the small intestines protruding from a transverse rent six inches in length a little below the navel. An attempt was made to return them at once, but the struggling of the patient and the pain occasioned by the pressure of the fingers became intolerable, as to render any further persistence in this plan quite impracticable. Chloroform was next exhibited and having no longer to encounter the former difficulties the parts were gradually returned to their normal position, save that portion of the lacerated intestine which was secured to the upper angle of the wound.[10]

It was never discovered how the wound came to be inflicted and after nearly two months, at a moment when her nurse was absent, Lucy again 'succeeded in tearing open the former wound and displacing an additional portion of intestine', and at this stage it was decided to secure her hands so that she was physically unable to touch her body. She lingered on until December 1851 when she died. This was not recorded as a case of suicide but, it is reasonable to suppose, that Lucy's death occurred as a result of her brutal attack upon her own body.

Between 1851 and 1870 there were only two confirmed cases of suicide recorded amongst the female patients. The earliest being in March 1857. Elizabeth Coates, aged 44 and single, was admitted to the asylum a month earlier with the cause described as change of life, but later diagnosed as suicidal melancholia.[11]

During the fortnightly dance, held on 3 March, Elizabeth went outside to the exercise court and hanged herself from a railing using a small piece of tape. The Coroner's Court, although they attached no blame to anyone, recommended that the railing be removed.

The physiognomy of mental diseases.

The second suicide occurred in March 1864. Mary Wilson, aged 37 and single, was admitted with mania on 25 February 1864.[12] On 2 March, the medical superintendent recorded in his report to the Committee of Visitors that

In November 1882, when Hannah went into the asylum on the ninth occasion, she was 54 years old, had borne thirteen children, six of whom had died. She weighed only 7 st. 9 lb. Within just one month she had settled down, and was described as quiet, industrious and rational in every way. Employed in the kitchen, she worked very industriously, which was always accepted as a sign of mental wellbeing, and was said to enjoy very good health. After four months she was sent out on probation and discharged as recovered in April 1883. Her weight had increased to 8 st. 13 lb.—eighteen pounds in five months.

Hannah Harvey in 1882 aged 54 (Norfolk Record Office SAH270).

However, the intervals between attacks shortened and the time she spent in the asylum increased although the pattern of her illness was unchanged; on admission she was restless, excited, noisy and destructive but within weeks she became good tempered, rational and quiet. Hannah died in the asylum in January 1901, aged 81.

Harriet Dann, a patient on five occasions, was first admitted when she was twenty-five years old in March 1858.[16] She returned in 1859 following the birth of her fourth child, the cause attributed to puerperal insanity. She was sent home recovered after eight months. Five years elapsed before her next admission, which was brief, just two months in the asylum before being discharged recovered. There followed another three years of well-being before re-admission, in May 1867, with the cause listed as poverty. On this occasion, she remained in the asylum five years before discharge. Her final admission was sixteen months later, in September 1873, when it was noted she was the mother of seven children, the youngest 12 weeks old, her weight 7 st. 10 lb., and she was 'badly nourished'. Immediately on admission her health improved:

> She works very well in the laundry and is very useful. She is apparently pretty nearly well now. Is essentially being cheerful, rational, contented and was no trouble whatever. Under ordinary circumstances she would therefore be discharged, but as she invariably relapses when sent out, is in every way better in the asylum than out of it, she will at all events be kept on here for the present. Her bodily health is very good and she has gained flesh of late.[17]

Both Hannah Harvey and Harriet Dann were employed in the asylum laundry during their treatment, both receiving favourable comments on the quality of their work.

Unfortunately the physical strain of bearing seven children in poverty was too much for Harriet's constitution and she began to develop symptoms of tuberculosis from which she eventually died in June 1877.

Laundry Room at Claybury Asylum, Woodford.

Susannah Phillippo, a patient admitted in 1870 and the subject of a case study in the previous chapter (see p. 48ff), was another example of frequent re-admission who, at the time of her reception in 1870, was diagnosed with parturition as the cause of her breakdown. She spent fourteen months in the asylum before being discharged as recovered and was re-admitted in October 1872 when it was recorded that she had a 'predisposition' to attacks of mania and she remained as a patient for two years on that occasion. After her husband's death in 1897, Susannah returned once more to the asylum in 1901 where she remained until her death in 1910. Whilst her first admission, as a married woman, was attributed to a cause resulting from childbirth, Susannah had a history of mental disorder dating back to 1857. She first entered the asylum at the age of twenty with the cause of insanity attributed to 'fright', and again in 1862 when the cause was unknown. When looking at the entire history of her mental illness, Susannah's malady required more than the asylum regime of regular nourishment, rest and exercise, to which many female patients with gendered diagnoses responded so well.

Most patients hoped for an early discharge so that they might return home but that was dependent on their home circumstances and there were some who preferred the security of the asylum. Jane Frost was admitted in October 1868 with the menopause or 'climacteric' as it was described, as the cause of her breakdown and by August 1870, when she was recommended for discharge, her condition had improved. On 30 August the medical officer noted:

> Today she showed great unwillingness to leave the asylum and complained that we were discharging her before she was well and able to earn her living. After it was made clear to her that for a time the parish would allow her four shillings a week and that instead of being discharged she would be sent out on probation only, she brightened up, dried her tears which had flowed copiously, the intense pain in her head magically disappeared; her spirits rose with the occasion and she left the asylum a perfectly rational and sane woman and to all appearances contented, if not happy.

Jane Frost was discharged recovered in October 1870 after a successful probationary period.

Another patient wishing to remain in the asylum was Mary Ann Goldsmith (see p. 39ff) admitted in February 1869 with delusions that she was the daughter of the Queen of England.[18] In May 1869 when she was told 'she would be discharged next Sunday she expressed herself as being quite contented with her present abode and was not willing to leave.' She was discharged at the end of May on a month's probation but was back before the month expired, not having progressed satisfactorily. Mary Ann was to spend the next twenty-two years in the asylum, still a patient there at the time of the 1891 census, and after that length of time unlikely to recover.

On returning to their former domestic situation, patients often lapsed into another spell of insanity resulting in their re-admission to the asylum. In 1864, the medical superintendent commented forcefully on the issue of re-admissions:

> The malady almost invariably arises from DEBILITY; now as many of the patients, on being discharged, return to hard work, still harder fare, and the anxieties attending the support of their families; can it be wondered at, that all these debilitating influences acting upon a nervous system so recently out of tune, should cause a relapse?[19]

To those who worked within the asylum system there seems to have been an understanding of the hardships experienced by the poor and a realisation that recovery was a precarious condition.

Caroline Ebbage was first admitted to the asylum in 1868 when the youngest of her five children was two months old. She was suffering mentally and physically from malnutrition as a result of poverty. She recovered but was readmitted two years later in the same condition, having another infant to breastfeed. Her third and final admission came in 1871—heavily pregnant once more. She gave birth in the asylum, but did not recover her physical health and her death followed in 1872. Caroline was another victim of phthisis, which in 1872 was the cause of 28 percent of all Norfolk asylum deaths.

Two other patients discussed in this chapter, Harriet Dann and Maria Freestone, also died from this cause. According to a report published in 1892 by Dr Crookshank deaths from phthisis in asylums in the British Isles were 'four and a half times as high as among males and six and one-third times as high as among females in the general population at the age at which the phthisical mortality is at its maximum'.[20]

There were many patent medicines such as 'pulmonic syrup' that claimed to alleviate symptoms in the progress of consumption.

A final re-admission with a happy ending: after a troubled and inauspicious start, Harriet Kettle's life saw a remarkable change of circumstance.[21] Her story is of particular note because she was initially referred to the asylum by the Secretary of State, or Home Secretary as the post is now known, due to criminal charges. She was re-admitted to Norfolk asylum on four occasions and was also a prisoner in the Wymondham House of Correction, a prisoner in the Walsingham Bridewell and a patient in Bethlem Asylum, Lambeth. Following a discouraging sequence of events, Harriet's story resulted in a totally unexpected outcome.

Her life began in Gressenhall workhouse, which she left as soon as she was able, to make a living by prostitution. Prostitution being a criminal offence, she was sent to Walsingham gaol and from there to the asylum, by order of the Home Secretary. She was first seen at the asylum in July 1856 when she was twenty-one years old and it was noted:

An advertisement for Schenck's pulmonic syrup, one of the many medicines that purported to alleviate consumption.

> A case of remittent mania which has been coming on for an uncertain time and is ascribed solely to a naturally bad temper and from her irregular life, she having been a girl on the town in Norwich for sometime previous to her committal to prison for having assaulted the master of a workhouse during her abode there for a time. No hereditary taint known. She seems to have no settled delusions so far, merely paroxysms of maniacal excitement. At others quiet. She seems to have a strong suicidal tendency, have attempted it more than once.[22]

After being discharged from the asylum, in March 1857, she was re-admitted on four further occasions before an appearance at court in April 1861, when the *Norfolk Chronicle* reported:

> Harriet Kettle having on three [sic] occasions been removed from the prison to the asylum at Thorpe and not having at any time on her return manifested the least symptom of improvement, ... the case was represented to the Secretary of State who had ordered her removal to the Criminal Lunatic Asylum at St George's-in-the-Fields, London [Bethlem].

After six months at the Bethlem Hospital, Harriet was discharged as recovered

19   Norfolk Record Office SAH 28 (Annual Reports 1844-1876)

20   https://www.ncbi.nlm.nih.gov/pmc/articles/PMC2401985/?page=2# 1902 Oct 25; 2(2182): 1349–1351 (accessed December 2020)

21   Ibid 6

22   Ibid

Conclusion

THE nineteenth century asylum regime introduced a system that attempted to offer respite and relief to the impoverished mentally ill in the community. Whilst the patients featured in this book are all female the asylum population in Norfolk included both men and women throughout its history. Many of the causes of mental disorder were common to both genders: religious mania, intemperance, family troubles, work troubles, and underlying these issues was frequently the very real problem of poverty.

The causes recorded at the patients' admission were sometimes correct and sometimes, after closer monitoring of the patient, acknowledged by the medical staff to be a mistaken diagnosis and revised. Diagnostics within the realm of mental illness was still relatively unscientific at this time and practically dependent on the patients' physical appearance and demeanour at their reception.

The high proportion of gender-specific causes assigned to women, together with the unreliability of diagnosis in the Victorian era, meant the submission of 'women's problems' as the cause of mental disorder was a useful classification when no other explanation was apparent. These case studies, which focused on gender-specific conditions from the years between 1851 and 1870, serve to illustrate that women from all social classes were diagnosed as insane due preconceptions about their sex. Amongst this group there were those who were physically exhausted or ill, yet exhibited symptoms suggesting insanity. Some patients recovered in the asylum, notably Mary Jane Lemmon and Eliza Hooper, whilst others, suffering from incurable diseases, such as tuberculosis, died. It is tempting to believe that Fanny Craven and Elizabeth Westgate had genuinely suffered the gender-specific maladies diagnosed and were restored to health by the treatment they received.

Whatever the outcome, research suggests that the Norfolk asylum was a caring environment with a dedicated team of medical personnel committed to providing the best support and care available within the boundaries of medical knowledge at that time. In some cases they also provided a crude, but compassionate, safe place for those in poverty and unable to cope with the rigours of life.

Appendix

Gender-Specific Causes of Insanity at Norfolk Lunatic Asylum (NLA) 1850-1870

Cause of Insanity Years of Use	Definition	Number of Admissions
Accouchement 1867-1870	The action of giving birth to a baby.	6
Amenorrhoea All years	The term used to describe a lack of 'periods' (menstrual cycles) in women.	9
Change of life 1855-1861	Known as the menopause, when menstrual periods cease. A term first used in 1761 and when applied to patients at NLA it implied emotional symptoms, such as memory problems, irritability and rapid changes in mood.	25
Childbirth 1850-1852	This remains in current use.	10
Climacteric 1862-1870	Has a similar meaning to 'change of life', implying the menopause or a time of great change.	12
Confinement 1854-1861	Another word in use today. In medical terms it suggests a time of lying-in after giving birth.	2
Hysteria 1858-1870	Historically, hysteria was thought to manifest itself in women (female hysteria) with a variety of symptoms including anxiety; shortness of breath; fainting; insomnia; irritability; nervousness; as well as sexually forward behaviour, a view prevalent in the mid-nineteenth century.	4
Lactation 1863-1870	Breastfeeding	9
Menorrhagia 1855	Excessive menstrual blood loss leading to anaemia.	1
Miscarriage 1868	As in in current use.	1
Parturition 1856-1870	Childbirth, labour and delivery.	26
Pregnancy 1859-1870	As in current use.	2
Puerperal 1857-1870	A fever occurring soon after childbirth and much feared in the nineteenth century. In the majority of patients the disease appeared on the third day, and commenced with rigour, headache and the "cold fit" followed by extreme heat, perspiration and thirst. Abdominal pain was an almost ubiquitous feature and this began as a mild symptom, becoming increasingly severe over the duration of the disease and often resulting in fatality. The term 'puerperal' in itself indicates the six week period post-parturition and the majority of the cases recorded at NLA were puerperal insanity rather than puerperal fever.	22
Suckling child 1856	Breastfeeding.	1
Uterine disturbance 1865-1870	Irregular menstrual bleeding.	3
Total:		**133**

Glossary

Alienist	An archaic term for a psychiatrist.
Aperient	A laxative used to relieve constipation, eg, senna, bisacodyl or a saline laxative.
Blistering	Medical blistering, also sometimes known as vesiculation, raised a blister on the skin, and was thought to be an effective tool to deal with certain medical issues including hysteria, hypochonriasis, gout, fevers, as well as cases of insanity.[1] To achieve this medical blistering required applications of a fine powder usually composed of cantharides (a powerful-blistering substance often obtained from blister beetles, sometimes called Spanish Fly). Sometimes other stimulant ingredients, such as pepper, mustard-seed and verdigris, were also added.[2] It was thought that the malady would be expelled from the body through the pus that developed as the blister became infected.
Bromide	Bromide compounds, especially potassium bromide, were frequently used as sedatives in the nineteenth and early twentieth century.[3]
Chloral	Used in the nineteenth century to sedate.
Consumption	See Phthisis.
Costive	Constipated.
Dementia	A term often used in the nineteenth century as an alternative to insanity.
Digitalis	A drug prepared from the dried leaves of foxgloves and containing substances (notably digoxin and digitoxin) that stimulate the heart muscle.[4]
Dirty habits	Defecating and/or urinating without control.
Encephalomalacia	Softening or loss of brain parenchyma with or without surrounding gliosis, as a late manifestation of injury.
Epileptiform	Resembling epilepsy or its manifestations.[5]
Erysipelas	A form of cellulitis.
Lacteal	Relating to milk.
Laudanum	An alcoholic tincture (dilute solution) of opium that was used in European medical practice as an analgesic and sedative.[6]
Leeching	The application of a living leech to the skin in order to initiate blood flow or deplete blood from a localised area of the body.[7]
Lunacy	An obsolete term for a form of insanity characterised by alternating lucid and insane periods, believed to be influenced by phases of the moon.[8]
Mania	The symptoms include elevated mood (either euphoric or irritable), increased energy, decreased need and desire for sleep, and hyperactivity.[9]
Mesenteric vascular disease	A condition that develops when the arteries in the abdomen that supply the intestines with blood become narrowed due to the build-up of plaque (a process called atherosclerosis). The result is a lack of blood supply to the intestines.
mischievous c. 1300	Evil condition, misfortune; hardship, need, want; wickedness, wrongdoing, evil, from Old French meschief: misfortune, harm, trouble; annoyance, vexation (12c., Modern French méchef).[10]
Morphia	Another name for morphine. Both morphia and morphine come from the name of Morpheus, the ancient god of sleep and dreams.
Opium	A reddish-brown heavy-scented addictive drug prepared from the juice of the opium poppy, used illicitly as a narcotic and occasionally in medicine as an analgesic
Packs	Packs consisting of sheets dipped in varying temperatures of water were wrapped around the patient for several hours (depending on the case), for a calming effect. The trend of hydrotherapy influenced this treatment.[11]
Phrenology	The study of human characteristics according to shape of the skull.[12]

Phthisis	Consumption and phthisis are terms used to refer to tuberculosis (TB) throughout history.[13] The modern era of tuberculosis treatment arrived with the discovery of streptomycin in 1944 and isoniazid in 1952.
Quinine	Used to treat malaria and sometimes restless leg syndrome.[14]
Sanguine	Optimistic, lively.
Seclusion	In asylum terms usually meaning isolation.
Viscera	The internal organs of the body specifically those within the chest or abdomen.[15]
Zinc	The chemical element of atomic number 30, a silvery-white metal that is a constituent of brass and is used for coating (galvanizing) iron and steel to protect against corrosion.

Notes

1   https://www.geriwalton.com/medical-blistering (accessed June 2020)

2   https://www.geriwalton.com/medical-blistering-in-georgian-era/ (accessed August 2020)

3   https://en.wikipedia.org/wiki/Bromide (accessed June 2020)

4   Oxford Languages and Google (accessed June 2020)

5   https://medical-dictionary.thefreedictionary.com/epileptiform (accessed June 2020)

6   https://www.britannica.com/science/laudanum (accessed June 2020)

7   https://www.britannica.com/science/leeching (accessed June 2020)

8   https://medical-dictionary.thefreedictionary.com/lunacy (accessed June 2020)

9   http://creativecommons.org/licenses/by-sa/3.0/ (accessed June 2020)

10   https://www.etymonline.com/word/mischief (accessed June 2020)

11   https://www.lib.uwo.ca/archives/virtualexhibits/londonasylum/hydrotherapy.html (accessed June 2020)

12   https://en.wikipedia.org/wiki/Phrenology (accessed June 2020)

13   https://www.sciencedirect.com/science/article/pii/s095461110600401x (accessed June 2020)

14   https://en.wikipedia.org/wiki/Quinine (accessed June 2020)

15   https://www.medicinenet.com/script/main/art.asp?articlekey=18276 (accessed June 2020)

Bibliography

Primary Sources

Norfolk Record Office SAH 28, Annual Report, 1854-73

Norfolk Record Office SAH 130, Master's Journal/Report Book March 1860-June 1861

Norfolk Record Office SAH 131 Medical Superintendent's Journals 1861-1872

Norfolk Record Office SAH 260 Case Book December 1848-April 1853

Norfolk Record Office SAH 262 Female Case Book March 1853-August 1861

Norfolk Record Office SAH 263 Case Book August 1861-December 1865

Norfolk Record Office SAH 264 Case Book December 1865-April 1870

Norfolk Record Office SAH 265 Case Book April 1870-June 1874

Norfolk Record Office SAH 267 Case Book May 1876-June 1878

Norfolk Record Office SAH 268 Case Book June 1878-March 1880

Norfolk Record Office SAH 270 Case Book September 1881-March 1883

Norfolk Record Office SAH 285 Case Book January 1885-June 1888

Norfolk Chronicle, 6 April, 1861

Norfolk Chronicle and Norwich Gazette, 26 August, 1871

Secondary Sources

A. Campbell Clark, C. McIvor Campbell, A. R. Turnbull, and A. R. Urquhart, *Handbook for the Instruction of Attendants on the Insane* (London, 1885)

S. Cherry, *Mental Health Care in Modern England, The Norfolk Lunatic Asylum/St Andrew's Hospital c 1810-1998* (Woodbridge, 2003)

A. Digby, *Pauper Palaces* (London, 1978)

D. Fraser, (ed), *The Christian Watt Papers* (Edinburgh, 2004)

H. Marland, 'Disappointment and desolation: women, doctors and interpretations of puerperal insanity in the nineteenth century', *History of Psychiatry, 14(3)*, 2003

H. Marland, 'Languages and landscapes of emotion: motherhood and puerperal insanity in the nineteenth century' in FB Alberti (ed) *Medicine, Emotion and Disease 1700-1950* (Basingstoke, 2006)

J. Melling and B. Forsythe, *Politics of Madness, The State, Insanity and Society in England, 1845-1914* (Abindon, 2006)

Charlotte Perkins Gilmore, The Yellow Wallpaper(1890), *The Yellow Wallpaper and selected writings* (London, 2009)

E. Showalter, *The Female Malady: Women, Madness, and English Culture, 1830-1980* (London, 1985)

L.M. Springall, *Labouring Life in Norfolk Villages 1834-1914* (London, 1936)

S. Wade-Martins, *Changing Agriculture in Georgian and Victorian Norfolk* (Cromer, 2002)

S. and B. Webb, *English Poor Law History* (London, 1929)

D. Wright, 'Delusions of gender?: lay identification and clinical diagnosis of insanity in Victorian England', in J. Andrews and A. Digby (eds), *Sex and Seclusion, Class and Custody: Perspectives on Gender and Class in the History of British and Irish Psychiatry* (Amsterdam, 2004)

Websites

https://www.nationalarchives.gov.uk/currency-converter/ (accessed June 2020)

https://www.ancestry.co.uk/imageviewer/collections/6598/images/NFKRG12_1540_1542-0534?ssrc=&backlabel=Return (accessed August 2020)

https://www.ncbi.nlm.nih.gov/pmc/articles/PMC2401985/?page=2# 1902 Oct 25; 2(2182): 1349–1351 (accessed June 2020)

https://wellcomelibrary.org/item/b24952862#? (accessed July 2020)

https://www.oireachtas.ie/en/visit-and-learn/history-and-buildings/historical-documents/approaches-to-mental-health/#:~:text=The%20word%20%22lunatic%22%20was%20used,fashion%20during%20the%2018th%20century. (accessed July 2020)

https://scotlandspeople.gov.uk (accessed February 2020)

https://www.britannica.com/science/leeching (accessed May 2020)

https://en.wikipedia.org/wiki/Hysteria (accessed March 2020)

https://wellcomecollection.org/articles/W89GZBIAAN4yz1hQ (accessed May 2020)

https://www.caston-online.co.uk/acastonwalk1911.asp (accessed April 2020)

https://www.ncbi.nlm.nih.gov/pmc/articles/PMC1088248/ (accessed March 2020)

Surrey Marriage Bonds and Allegations records held by the London Metropolitan Archives (accessed via Ancestry February 2020)

England & Wales, National Probate Calendar (Index of Wills and Administrations), 1858-1995 (accessed February 2020)

https://www.healthline.com (accessed September 2020)

Index